19th & 20th Century Paintings

from the Collection of the

Smith College Museum of Art

CLAUDE MONET French, 1840-1926, *The Seine at Bougival*, 1869

19th & 20th Century Paintings

from the Collection of the

Smith College Museum of Art

Catalogue prepared by Mira Matherny Fabian

Michael Wentworth & Charles Chetham

A CIRCULATING EXHIBITION SPONSORED BY THE AMERICAN FEDERATION OF ARTS

Published by the Smith College Museum of Art,
Northampton, Massachusetts, 1970, with funds
provided by the Museum Members.

Library of Congress Catalog Card Number: 73-118586
Copyright © 1970 by Smith College Museum of Art
All rights reserved.
Printed in the United States of America

Acknowledgments

Fifty-eight paintings from the Smith College Museum of Art are touring the country because they, together with 9,000 additional paintings, drawings, prints, sculpture, and decorative arts which make up the collection, temporarily have no home. Smith College is in the midst of planning and building a new Art Complex. The building, designed by John Andrews of Toronto, will quadruple the present space allotted to the practice, the teaching of the history, and the collection of art at Smith. Most of the Museum's objects will be kept on the campus while the building is constructed and will be used in exhibitions and in teaching as space and time permit. The Trustees of the College have authorized the present tour in the hope that many thousands of persons who cannot make the trip to Northampton, will be able to see at least a portion of our collection. The American Federation of Arts has undertaken to circulate the collection through the country.

Despite the fact that the Museum owns works of art dating from the 5th century B.C. to the present, the selection has been limited to the 19th and 20th centuries for the sake of coherence. Our purpose is not only to show some of our finest paintings but also to exhibit the key examples which mark the growth of the collection historically. Therefore, we have included the first painting acquired, Thomas Eakins' *In Grandmother's Time*. The little Champney, *Boon Companions*, is a tribute to the first artist who helped Mr. Seelye with his search. Mr. Tryon's painting, *November Evening*, is a work by the founder of the collection. The small Chase, almost a masterpiece,

and the Hassam, a fine picture, illustrate the years when the collection was entirely American and entirely contemporary. Both the unfinished Ingres and the incomplete painting attributed to Bonington are realizations by Mr. Hitchcock of Mr. Churchill's pedagogic aim in acquiring partially finished works by great artists. Thus the selection should give the viewer with imagination not only aesthetic pleasure, but make him aware, at the same time, of the ideas that informed the growth of the collection.

The work presented here is the collaborative effort of Mrs. Robert Fabian, Assistant Curator of the Smith College Museum of Art, Michael Wentworth, Acting Director, and the writer. All had the arduous task of corroborating every entry. Mrs. Fabian also prepared the manuscript for the printer, and Mrs. Edward Sullivan typed the whole. In the spring of 1968, a group of Smith seniors who had enrolled in the Museum Seminar given by the writer began to collate material. They brought a degree of order to our files and added much new information. As is often the case, the experience was sometimes confusing to them and as frequently happens, their reward was not received in their time at Smith nor are their efforts presented here in the form in which it left their hands. However, their work was a considerable contribution to the whole. These students are: Diana Buitron, Susan Clarke, Charlotte Furstenberg, Cary MacRae, Virginia Scheer, and Kathryn Schwarzchild.

From this statement it is evident that the catalogue for the exhibition grew by accretion. The record presented here was pieced together over the years not only by the present staff of the Museum but by every former employee as well. The facts presented here have been checked as carefully as possible, but still error may persist. The basis for this catalogue is to be found in the old records which include the accessions book of the Museum, and the documentary files for each picture. As it often happens in under-staffed and over-worked museums where personnel changes frequently and can vanish with records kept in mind rather than on paper, the documentary files were luxuriant in their complexity and often in their contradiction. In addition to the files, we consulted the unpublished catalogue by Alfred Vance Churchill, *Authoritative List Containing Confidential Information*, of May 1916 (the confidential information was the insurance value of each object), the Handbook of 1925, the Catalogue of 1937 and its supplement of 1941.

Four years ago the writer revived the Museum Membership which had been active under the Directorships of Mr. Churchill and Mr. Abbott but which had since lain dormant. The purpose of the membership was to accumulate enough money to underwrite the publication of our collections. The catalogue presented here is the first such endeavor expressly paid for by those understanding friends and alumnae who have patiently waited to see their gifts turned to use.

Many other persons have been helpfully involved in the preparation of the exhibition and its tour of the country. Our special thanks are due to the staff of the American Federation of Arts for their help in the preparation and circulation of the exhibition. Roy Moyer, Director, and Robert Luck, Assistant Director, guided the preparation of the tour in every detail. William Sullivan, Circulation Consultant, handled all the details of booking the exhibition. R. Michael Shroyer, Registrar, and Charles Jones, Assistant Registrar, prepared the exhibition for travel, overseeing conservation, insurance, and shipping arrangements. We would also like to thank Konrad G. Kuchel, Exhibition Coordinator, Thelma Berozi, Mary Lanier, and Enid Winslow at the AFA for their helpfulness and kindness. David Brooke, Director of the Currier Gallery, Manchester, New Hampshire, and Hugh Gourley, Director, The Colby College Art Museum, Waterville, Maine, must receive our thanks. Additional recognition is due John Ittmann, Curatorial Assistant, The University of Kansas Museum of Art, Lawrence, and Mrs. Joachim Stieber, Mrs. William Kennick, Mrs. Harold Craig, Mrs. Jane Watts and Edward Russell, all of the Smith College Museum, for their help in the preparation of the exhibition and the catalogue; and to Richard Hendel, The University of Massachusetts Press, Amherst, the Meriden Gravure Company, Meriden, Connecticut, and Rainbows, Inc., Hazardville, Connecticut, for their design and production. We must also thank Thornton Rockwell, Museum Conservator, who prepared the pictures for travel and Hyman Edelstein who photographed most of the paintings; and Morton Vose of the Vose Galleries, Boston, Mrs. R. L. Howes, Administrative Assistant, The Smith College Archives, and Mrs. Marcia Bradley, College Archivist, for the many helpful services they performed.

Charles Chetham DIRECTOR

Smith College Museum of Art*

1

2

The Smith College Museum of Art could be styled a product of New England idealism and pragmatism. While other institutions can cite specific dates of incorporation or of founding, a search through our records proves that the idea of the collection existed before the first picture was purchased. The College (fig. 1) was founded in 1871 , and in 1872 the Trustees issued a circular stating that the curriculum would include the study of art and music. In 1877 the College received an offer, from an unknown donor, of $1000.00 for an art collection, with the provision that the Trustees should appropriate $4,000.00 for the same purpose. That sum was voted and $4,000.00 more was raised by subscription. In the same decade that saw the organization of the Museum of Fine Arts, Boston and the Metropolitan Museum, and at a time when the study and collecting of art in colleges was almost non-existent, Smith's first president, L. Clarke Seelye (1873-1910) (fig. 2), supported by friends of the College, laid plans for courses in art and for a museum.

Seelye was convinced of the importance of forming a collection of contemporary American art. He visited artists in their studios, stated his purpose and asked their co-operation. Their names constitute a Who's Who of late 19th century American painting. President Seelye constantly emphasized that the collection would be one wholly of American painting and would perhaps be the only one so formed. Artists

*This is a slightly revised version of the article which appeared in *Antiques*, November 1969, pp. 768-775. We are grateful to the Editor, Miss Alice Winchester ('29), for her kind permission to reprint it.

3

were sufficiently impressed with the man, his aims, and the educational value of their work to the institution. Many let their paintings go at half or one-third their customary prices, on the understanding that such concessions should not be made public. Even when pictures came from dealers, President Seelye recorded that they were bought after consultation with the artists and still at substantial reductions in cost. Among the artists visited were: Hassam, Thayer, Weir, Inness, Ryder, Dewing, Homer, Fuller, Chase, Wyant, Tarbell, J.G. Brown, F.E. and F.S. Church, Bellows and many others. Whether by design or by fortuitous accident, the very first picture ever acquired by the College was a small painting, *In Grandmother's Time* by Thomas Eakins (no. 19), a man now seriously judged the single greatest artist this country ever produced. In making his rounds, President Seelye had the help of the painter, J. Wells Champney (1843-1903), the first recorded teacher of drawing at Smith. Champney was engaged to come twice every week during six weeks of the fall term, and six weeks of the winter term, to give practical instruction in drawing as one of the optional studies, and a course of general lectures upon sculpture and painting to all the students. He was to receive for his services $20.00 a day.

In 1881 Winthrop Hillyer gave money to construct a building on condition that the $8,000.00 already raised should be used solely for the art collection (fig. 3). In 1882 the Hillyer Art Gallery was completed and became the home not only of the future collection but of the studios for the practice of art. At the time of Mr. Hillyer's death, in 1883, a memorandum was found in his desk. It indicated his intention of bequeathing a substantial sum for increasing the art collection. His surviving brother and sister, Mr. Drayton Hillyer and Sarah Hillyer Mather (Mrs. Roland

4

5

Mather) generously recognized this intentional legacy as if it were a legal document. In 1887 Mr. and Mrs. Hillyer (Carlotta Hart) and Mrs. Mather gave funds of their own for an addition to the building.

Spurred by Mr. Hillyer's donation, President Seelye persuaded Dwight Tryon (fig. 4) to come to Northampton in 1881 to teach art and to help with the collection. Tryon had just returned from five years of study in Paris at the school of Jacquesson de la Chevreuse, a pupil of Ingres. Perhaps as an antidote to this academic training, he adopted the current practice of the Impressionist and Barbizon painters and, while still in France, painted from nature. For criticism, he took his work to Daubigny and Guillemet. Tryon's classes in drawing and painting flourished at Smith. He became increasingly successful in his career as an artist and his collaboration with Mr. Seelye was crowned with harmony and success. One has to admit that an unusual moment in the history of collecting had been reached when a college president and a painter saw eye-to-eye.

For many years Smith collected only American pictures. In 1905, a chair for the History and Interpretation of Art was created and Alfred Vance Churchill (1864-1949) was appointed to it. He was twenty-six when he came to Smith and, like Tryon twenty-five years earlier, had just returned from years of painting in Europe where he had studied in Berlin, Leipzig and Paris. More history-minded than Tryon, he found the concentration on American art a limitation to his teaching. He later wrote, "Our collection was begun as a group of American paintings. No attempt was made to represent, by original works, the art of other times and countries. Casts and photographs were the sole resources of the Museum in those fields" (fig. 5). That situation began to alter in 1911 when a group of Smith undergraduates pre-

6

7

8

sented the collection with its first work of European art. According to Churchill, ". . . a group of famous etchings was exhibited at Smith College in 1911, particularly for the benefit of students in Art 14. To many of the students this was their first sight of prints by great artists, and when it was discovered that Smith College owned no etchings, an enthusiastic group, members of the Studio Club and their friends purchased a fine proof of the fourth state of the *Three Crosses* by Rembrandt and gave it to the gallery "(fig. 6).

By 1914 the College had committed itself to the collecting of European art. This was doubtless influenced by Churchill's own interests and confirmed by Dwight Tryon's stated intention of leaving his fortune to Smith. Perhaps as a celebration of the change in focus, Churchill turned to the then greatest living sculptor, Auguste Rodin, and purchased a small bronze, the *Brother and Sister* (fig. 7). Many singular, even unique works were added during Mr. Churchill's tenure. Although it is vulgar to mention money in the same breath with art (curiously, one rarely hears of an object today without its price-tag) the most extraordinary purchase price-wise was the Lehmbruck *Torso* (fig. 8). Acquired in 1922, itself an unusual date for an American institution to buy a Lehmbruck, it cost the College $125.00 (discussions of price end here.)

Churchill's acquisitions include the Courbet, *La Toilette de la mariée* (no. 14); the Corot, *Jumièges* (no. 11); the Cézanne, *La Route tournante à La Roche-Guyon* (no. 8), and the *Portrait of Mrs. Mahon* by Thomas Eakins (no. 20).

In 1920, before any of these acquisitions had been made, Mr. Churchill was appointed Director of the "Smith College Museum of Art." The Trustees had concurred with his plan to enlarge the scope of the

Museum and he was allowed five months travel in Europe expressly to buy for the collection. He was instructed, "not to buy expensive masterpieces, but to illustrate the history of civilization through works of art." Perhaps he found this a pretty tall order for he shortly thereafter devised what became known as the "concentration plan." In the Museum *Bulletin* of 1932, he wrote, "It seemed to me that attention must be devoted, first of all, to the cultures from which our own is derived and on which it rests—Egypt, Greece, Rome and the rest, down through the Renaissance. We must follow the main stream of western civilization. But even this area was impossibly vast while its chief phases might eventually be illustrated with a few examples we could never do justice to all. The only practicable plan was to do what we could for the great historic periods and to choose a limited field for more adequate representation . . . So a college museum might hope to acquire 'something' of every period, and richer and fuller illustrations (if not everything) of one of them . . . My proposal was this: let us select, not a nation or school but a *topic*—The Development of Modern Art . . . assume modern art begins with the period of the French Revolution . . . The break with the past has never been more complete." From that date, museum acquisition policy pursued these two goals: first, a distribution covering the chief phases of western civilization and second, a concentration on the 19th and early 20th century.

Churchill's "painter's mind" led him into the habit of buying partially finished works of art. He reasoned that sketches and partially finished paintings provided students and teachers with a graph of the creative act, a record which, more often than not, was hidden in an artist's finished work. He recognized, on the one hand, that trustees of most museums would not covet "unfinished" works and that, on the other hand,

9

10

11

Smith's resources would never allow it to compete with her larger sisters. He referred to his position vis-à-vis that of major museums: "I was willing to acquire a *fragment* where they would not, for even a fragment may reveal the master. I would take an *unfinished work* where they would not, for such work may convey quite as much as a finished one."

Throughout his tenure, the third President of Smith College, William Allan Neilson (1917-1939) (fig. 9), was intensely interested in the Museum. Neilson was counsellor and colleague of both Mr. Churchill and Jere Abbott who was to become the Museum's second director (1932-1946). Although there is no record of his visiting studios in the manner of Seelye, it is clear that in 1929, Mr. Neilson strongly supported Mr. Churchill's proposal for acquiring the most important, most expensive and largest painting the College had thus far considered: the unfinished Courbet, *La Toilette de la mariée* (no. 14). Neilson reasoned that the collection needed one major work of indisputable quality. Such a commitment by the College would again underline its faith in the usefulness of art to education. Furthermore, Neilson was heard to say, "Where there are great works of art, others will follow." He was certainly correct.

In 1925, Dwight Tryon and his wife had presented the College with the money for a new museum building, the Tryon Gallery, but he did not live to see it completed (fig. 10). His widow came to Northampton to help arrange the memorial gallery of Tryon's paintings, but she refused to participate in a formal inauguration of the building. The modesty and the idealism of the pair is explicit in the dedicatory plaque at the Museum's entrance, which reads, "That the students of this college may know in their youth the solace and inspiration of Art, Dwight William Tryon and Alice Belden Tryon have dedicated to them this

12

13

14

15

building, 1925." The Tryons also bequeathed the funds to Smith which allowed it to act when the great Courbet came on the market.

If Mr. Churchill established the theoretical basis for collecting at Smith and set a high standard for actual acquisition, Jere Abbott, who came to Northampton in 1932 after three years as a founding member of the Museum of Modern Art, is responsible for acquiring a sequence of excellent School of Paris objects and at the same time enlarging the scope of the collection by obtaining works from the 14th through the 19th centuries. These paintings, drawings and sculptures, so varied in their style, have in common an exceptionally high level of quality. Among Mr. Abbott's acquisitions are found (to cite only a few): the Degas, *Jephthah's Daughter* (fig. 11) and the *Portrait of René de Gas* (no. 16); the Corot, *La Blonde Gasconne* (no. 12) of which one irate alumna wrote "Moral leprosy . . . in life this creature is a fat, sensual, immodest, soulless piece of clay. What makes her *picture* anything but disgusting—as Lord Byron would say— 'to have spat out of the mouth'?." Mr. Abbott's first purchase was the Picasso, *La Table* (no. 44). In 1932, that year of depression and not much permissiveness, it set as many teeth on edge as the charming Corot. The range of Mr. Abbott's interests allowed him to respond to the Seurat oil sketch for the *Grande Jatte* (no. 53), the glorious Monet, *Seine at Bougival* (no. 39), the Vuillard, *Intérieur à l'Etang-la-Ville* (no. 57), the Calder, *Mobile* (fig. 12), and to the van Goyen, *View of Rijnland* (fig. 13) as well. His sensitivity to drawing brought to the College the Ingres, *Provost and Leclère* (fig. 14) and our most renowned drawing, the 15th century silver point *Portrait of a Young Man* by Dieric Bouts (fig. 15). Mr. Abbott did not actually establish the drawing collection, but his acquisitions provided the incentive for the many fine additions that followed.

16

17

18

19

20

21

Subsequent directors have pursued special interests. There is some truth in the suggestion that Smith's collection is a sum of the personal interests of its various directors, advisors and donors. Frederick Hartt (acting director, 1946-47) bought the Rigaud, *Duc d'Estrées* (fig. 16); during Edgar Schenck's directorship (1947-49), the *Gallienus* (fig. 17) was acquired. The distinguished architectural historian, Henry-Russell Hitchcock (1949-55) was particularly interested in English art. He added numerous works of quality, often with architectural elements predominating. Good examples are the Wright of Derby, *Cavern: Evening* (fig. 18), the Bellotto, *View of a Palace Courtyard* (fig. 19) and the Hubert Robert, *Pyramids* (fig. 20). Robert Parks (1955-1961) purchased the Kirchner, *Dodo and her Brother* (no. 31), the Grünewald drawing, *Study of Drapery* (fig. 21), and the Terbrugghen, *Old Man Reading* (fig. 22). The splendid full length Gilbert Stuart, *Portrait of Henrietta Vane* (fig. 23) and the classic Arp, *Torso* (fig. 24) were given to the collection at this time. During the writer's tenure, the collection has seen the additions of the Fantin-Latour, *Portrait of Mr. Becker* (no. 22), the Romako, *Girl on a Swing* (no. 48), the Menzel drawing, *Old Man with a Glass* (fig. 25), the Kline, *Rose, Purple and Black* (no. 32), the blue period Picasso, *Les Misérables* (no. 45), and the Mondrian, *Chrysanthemum* (fig. 26).

Today, the Museum is known chiefly for its paintings by French masters of the 19th and 20th centuries, but it includes art from all periods of history. True to Mr. Churchill's intentions it does have 'something' of everything with objects from Egypt, Greece, Rome, medieval France and Germany, Renaissance pictures from Italy and Baroque and modern works from most countries of western Europe. The collections of English and American pictures rival our French collection

22

23

24

25

26

in their completeness. Our inventory lists approximately 9,000 paintings, drawings, sculpture and prints. Smith students use the Museum regularly, either in scheduled class meetings, or by attending our frequent exhibitions or events, or by becoming a part of a museum seminar which works in the collection. We agree with Mr. Churchill that a college museum could not, and probably should not attempt to illustrate the entire history of form. This is an objective for the greatest general museums only. Once it might have been necessary to be concerned with our own cultural "mainstream," but now we have developed the capacity and the responsibility to value arts of widely different cultures — we now collect oriental and African art, neither of which was included in the original concentration plan. We are cognizant of the new arts which emphasize the validity of all human expression through plastic form, whether it be reason, clarity, emotional excess, physiological response to stimuli, accident, or play. In all our efforts the College has been aided and abetted by loyal alumnae who came to Northampton as students, absorbed the meaning of art, as well as its "solace and inspiration" and have returned many times over the debt they feel to Smith College and to the collection.

Charles Chetham DIRECTOR

Catalogue

COMPILERS' NOTE

All photographs were made directly from the originals. We have included many references to exhibitions for which no catalogue was prepared. The Smith College Museum of Art has often lent to educational institutions whose resources have not always allowed a publication to accompany an exhibition. We have also lent to colleges for classroom instruction where no formal exhibition was held. These instances have been recorded by listing the name of the college alone. Accession numbers which incorporate the year of acquisition are recorded as part of each entry. The Smith College Museum of Art is abbreviated as SCMA throughout all entries.

Abbreviations

Exhibitions

Chicago, AIC, 1933
Art Institute of Chicago, 1933, *A Century of Progress.*

London, Lefèvre, 1934
London, Alex. Reid & Lefèvre, Ltd., 1934, *Renoir, Cézanne and their Contemporaries.*

SCMA, *Corot*, 1934
SCMA, 1934, *Exhibition of Portraits and Early Landscapes by J.B.C. Corot.* [Catalogue published in SCMA *Bulletin*, 1935, pp. 19-28.]

Hartford, 1935
Hartford, Wadsworth Atheneum, 1935, *American Painting and Sculpture: Three Centuries.*

Chicago, AIC, 1938-39
Art Institute of Chicago, 1938-39, *A Loan Exhibition of Paintings and Prints by Pierre Bonnard and Edouard Vuillard.*

Boston, IMA, 1939
Boston, Institute of Modern Art, 1939, *The Sources of Modern Painting.*

Chicago, Arts Club, 1939
Arts Club of Chicago, 1939, *Juan Gris 1887-1927.*

Wildenstein, 1943
New York, Wildenstein, 1943, *From Paris to the Sea Down the River Seine.*

Andover, 1945
Andover, Massachusetts, Addison Gallery of American Art, 1945, *A Way of Painting which Became a Way of Seeing.*

SCMA, *Churchill* 1946
SCMA, 1946, *Exhibition in Honor of Alfred Vance Churchill.*

MOMA, 1948
New York, Museum of Modern Art and Cleveland Museum of Art, 1948, *Pierre Bonnard.* [Catalogue by John Rewald]

Wildenstein, 1948
New York, Wildenstein, 1948, *Six Masters of Post-Impressionism.*

Wildenstein, 1948-49
New York, Wildenstein, 1948-49, *Gustave Courbet.*

Wellesley, 1949-50
Wellesley [Massachusetts] College, Farnsworth Museum, 1949-50.

Dartmouth, 1950
Hanover, New Hampshire, Dartmouth College, 1950, *Contemporary Painting.* [To accompany a lecture by Meyer Shapiro before the Great Issues Course.]

Detroit, 1950
Detroit Institute of Arts, 1950, *French Painting from David to Courbet.*

Williams, 1950
Williamstown, Massachusetts, Williams College, Lawrence Art Museum, 1950, *Sixteen Portraits (1600-1900).*

Wesleyan, 1951
Middletown, Connecticut, Wesleyan University, Davison Art Center, 1951, *Aspects of American Realism.*

Montreal, 1952
Montreal Museum of Fine Arts, 1952, *Six Centuries of Landscape.*

Amherst, 1953
Amherst [Massachusetts] College, Mead Art Building, 1953, *Impressionism.*

Knoedler, 1953 — New York, Knoedler, 1953, *Paintings and Drawings from the Smith College Collection.*

Syracuse, 1953 — Syracuse Museum of Fine Arts, 1953, *125 Years of American Art.*

Boston, ICA, 1954 — Boston, The Institute of Contemporary Art, 1954, *Forty-Four Major Works from the Smith College Collection.* [Checklist published in The Institute of Contemporary Art Bulletin, Jan./Feb., 1954]

Detroit, 1954 — Detroit Institute of Arts, 1954, *The Two Sides of the Medal: French Painting from Gerome to Gauguin.*

Lyon, 1954 — Musée des Beaux-Arts de Lyon, 1954, *Courbet.*

Winnipeg, 1954 — Winnipeg [Manitoba] Art Gallery, 1954, *French Pre-Impressionist Painters of the Nineteenth Century.*

Wildenstein, 1955 — New York, Wildenstein, 1955, *A Special Exhibition of Paintings by American and French Modern Masters.*

Mount Holyoke, 1956 — South Hadley, Massachusetts, Mount Holyoke College, Dwight Art Memorial, 1956, *French and American Impressionism.*

University Collections, 1956-57 — *University Collections, 1956-57.* A circulating exhibition sponsored by the College Art Association and assembled by The American Federation of Arts. Exhibited: Malmö Rådhus; Utrecht Centraal Museum; Birmingham, City Art Gallery; London, University of London, Senate House; Newcastle upon Tyne, Hatton Gallery; Brussels, Palais des Beaux-Arts; Liège, Musée des Beaux-Arts; Marburg, University Museum; Tübingen, University Library and Besançon, Musée Bonnat. [Editions of the catalogue were published in New York, Malmö, Utrecht, Brussels, Lyon and Marburg. Our references are to the American edition.]

Amherst, Jones Library, 1958 — Amherst, Massachusetts, Jones Library, 1958, *American Art I, II.* [An exhibition in connection with the Armory Retrospective at Amherst College, Mead Art Building.]

Wesleyan, 1958 — Middletown, Connecticut, Wesleyan University, Davison Art Center, 1958, *Summer Exhibition.*

AFA, 1959-60 — The American Federation of Arts, 1959-60, *Major Work in Minor Scale.* Exhibited in: Jacksonville [Florida] Art Museum; Des Moines [Iowa] Art Center; Tulsa, Oklahoma, Philbrook Art Center; Seattle, Washington, Charles and Emma Fry Museum; Victoria, British Columbia, Art Gallery of Greater Victoria; Ithaca, New York, Andrew Dickson White Museum of Art; Miami Beach, Florida, Miami Art Center; Joplin, Missouri, Spiva Art Center; Evansville [Indiana] Museum of Arts and Sciences; Pittsburgh, Chatham College; New Britain, Connecticut, Art Museum of the New Britain Institute.

Philadelphia-Boston, 1959-60
Philadelphia Museum of Art and Boston, Museum of Fine Arts, 1959-60, *Gustave Courbet*.

Chicago, AIC, 1960
Art Institute of Chicago, 1960, *Corot*.

Cleveland, 1960
Cleveland Museum of Art, 1960, *Paths of Abstract Art*.

New Bedford, 1960
New Bedford, Massachusetts, William W. Crapo Gallery, Swain School of Design, 1960, *A Selection of Paintings by Albert Pinkham Ryder and Albert Bierstadt*.

Williams, 1960
Williamstown, Massachusetts, Williams College, Lawrence Art Museum, 1960, *Symposium on American Art*.

Chicago, Arts Club, 1961
Arts Club of Chicago, 1961, *Smith College Loan Exhibition*.

SCMA, *Portraits*, 1962
SCMA, 1962, *Portraits from the Collection of the Smith College Museum of Art*.

Minneapolis, 1963-64
Minneapolis Institute of Arts, 1963-64, *Four Centuries of American Art*.

Chicago, NDC, 1964
Chicago, National Design Center, Marina City, 1964, *Four Centuries of Portraits*.

SCMA, *American Painting*, 1964
SCMA, 1964, *An Exhibition of American Painting for a Professor of American Art*. [An exhibition honoring Professor Oliver Larkin.]

MOMA, 1964-65
New York, Museum of Modern Art, 1964, Art Institute of Chicago and Los Angeles County Museum, 1965, *Bonnard and his Environment*. [Catalogue by James Thrall Soby, James Elliott and Monroe Wheeler]

Edinburgh-London, 1965
Edinburgh, Royal Scottish Academy and London, National Gallery, 1965, *Corot* [Sponsored by the Edinburgh Festival Society and arranged by the Arts Council of Great Britain in association with the Royal Scottish Academy]

Mount Holyoke, 1965
South Hadley, Massachusetts, Mount Holyoke College, Dwight Art Memorial, 1965, *Nineteenth Century American Landscape Paintings*.

Colby-Williams, 1966
Waterville, Maine, Colby College Art Museum and Williamstown, Massachusetts, Williams College Museum of Art, 1966, *Art in the Making*.

New York, PEA, 1966
New York, Public Education Association, 1966, *Seven Decades, 1895-1965: Crosscurrents in Modern Art*.

Trenton, 1967
Trenton, New Jersey State Museum Cultural Center, 1967, *Focus on Light*.

Amherst, 1968
Amherst [Massachusetts] College, Mead Art Building, 1968, *Art for Study: The Modern Tradition*.

Baltimore, 1968
Baltimore Museum of Art, 1968, *From El Greco to Pollock: Early and Late Works by European and American Artists*.

SCMA, *Hitchcock*, 1968
SCMA, 1968 *An Exhibition in Honor of Henry-Russell Hitchcock*.

Colby-Currier, 1969
Waterville, Maine, Colby College Art Museum and Manchester, New Hampshire, Currier Gallery of Art, 1969, *Nineteenth and Twentieth Century Paintings from the Smith College Museum of Art*.

References

Robaut, 1906 — Alfred Robaut and Etiènne Moreau Nélaton, *L'Oeuvre de Corot*, Paris, 1905.

Widener Coll., 1915 — W. Roberts, *Pictures in the Collection of P.A.B. Widener of Lynnewood Hall, Elkins Park, Pennsylvania: British and Modern French Schools*, privately printed, Philadelphia, 1915.

Churchill, 1916 — Alfred Vance Churchill, *Authoritative List Containing Confidential Information*, unpublished (1916).

Lugt — Fritz Lugt, *Les Marques de collections de dessins et d'estampes*, Amsterdam, 1921, Supplement, 1956.

SCMA *Handbook*, 1925 — Alfred Vance Churchill, *Handbook of the Art Collections of Smith College: Paintings, Sculpture, Drawings, Prints, Ceramics, Textiles*, Northampton, 1925.

Léger, 1929 — Charles Léger, *Courbet*, Paris, 1929.

Pennsylvania Mus. *Bull.*, 1930 — "Catalogue of the Works of Thomas Eakins," The Pennsylvania Museum *Bulletin*, vol. XXV, no. 133, March 1930, pp. 17-33.

Courthion, 1931 — Pierre Courthion, *Courbet*, Paris, 1931.

Churchill, 1932 — Alfred Vance Churchill, "Our Concentration Plan," SCMA *Bulletin*, 1932, pp. 1-22.

Goodrich, 1933 — Lloyd Goodrich, *Thomas Eakins, His Life and Work*, New York, 1933.

Zervos, 1934 — Christian Zervos, "Les Exposi-tions—Renoir, Cézanne, leurs contemporains et la jeune peinture anglaise," *Cahiers d'Art*, vol. 9. nos. 5-8, 1934, pp. 125-[136].

Abbott, 1935 — Jere Abbott, "The Two Corots," SCMA *Bulletin*, 1935, pp. 1-19.

SCMA *Catalogue*, 1937 — Jere Abbott, *Smith College Museum of Art Catalogue*, Northampton, 1937.

Abbott, 1939 — Jere Abbott, "Classics and Moderns at Smith: A Mosaic and French Paintings for the College Museum," *Art News*, vol. XXXVII, no. 17, January 21, 1939, pp. 6-7, 20.

Wilenski, 1940 — R.H. Wilenski, *Modern French Painters*, New York, n.d. [1940].

SCMA *Catalogue Supplement*, 1941 — *Smith College Museum of Art, Supplement to the Catalogue of 1937*, Northampton, 1941.

Cheney, 1941 — Sheldon Cheney, *The Story of Modern Art*, New York, 1941.

McKinney, 1942 — Roland J. McKinney, *Thomas Eakins*, New York, 1942.

Rewald, 1942 — John Rewald, "For Bonnard on His Seventy-Fifth Birthday," *Art News*, vol. XLI, October 1, 1942, pp. 23-25.

Shoolman-Slatkin, 1942 — Regina Shoolman and Charles E. Slatkin, *The Enjoyment of Art in America*, Philadelphia, 1942.

Lemoisne, 1946 — Paul A. Lemoisne, *Degas et son oeuvre*, Paris, 1946.

Hartt, 1947 — Frederick Hartt, "A Manet and a Monet," SCMA *Bulletin*, 1947, pp. 3-8.

Larkin, 1949 — Oliver W. Larkin, *Art and Life in America*, New York, 1949, [rev. ed. 1960.]

Zervos, 1949   Christian Zervos, *Picasso*, Paris, 1949.

Mack, 1951   Gerstle Mack, *Gustave Courbet*, New York, 1951.

Frankenstein, 1953   Alfred Frankenstein, *After the Hunt: William Harnett and Other American Still Life Painters, 1870-1900*, Berkeley, 1953 [2nd rev. ed., Honolulu, 1969].

Hitchcock, 1953   Henry-Russell Hitchcock, "New Pictures at Museum of Art," *Smith Alumnae Quarterly*, vol. XLIV, no. 2, February 1953.

SCMA, *Forty French Pictures*, 1953   *Forty French Pictures in the Smith College Museum of Art* [Foreword by George Heard Hamilton], Northampton, 1953.

Sicre, 1954   José Gómez Sicre, *Guía de las Colecciones Publicas de Arte en Los Estados Unidos*, Washington, 1954.

Faison, 1958   S. Lane Faison, Jr., *A Guide to the Art Museums of New England*, New York, 1958.

Guitar, 1959   Mary Anne Guitar, "Treasures on Campus," *Mademoiselle*, vol. 49, May 1959, pp. 112-115.

Chetham, 1965   Charles Chetham, "Seeing Past the Book End," *Smith Alumnae Quarterly*, vol. LVI, no. 2, Winter 1965, pp. 73-76.

Dauberville, 1965   Jean and Henri Dauberville, *Bonnard: Catalogue raisonné de l'oeuvre peint*, Paris, 1965, 2 vols. [vol. III forthcoming].

Chetham, 1969   Charles Chetham, "The Smith College Museum of Art," *Antiques*, vol. XCVI, no. 5, November 1969, pp. 768-775.

Novak, 1969   Barbara Novak, *American Painting of the Nineteenth Century*, New York, 1969.

Anonymous
French, 19th century

1. *Portrait of a Youth*
c. 1815
Oil on canvas, 17¾ x 14¼ inches
Purchased 1931:6

PROVENANCE
Percy Moore Turner, London, to SCMA.

EXHIBITIONS
Buffalo, Albright Art Gallery, 1932, *Nineteenth Century French Art in Retrospect 1800-1900*, no. 29, illus. pl. IV; Hartford, Wadsworth Atheneum, 1934, *Nineteenth Century French Painting*, p. 9; Boston, IMA, 1939, no. 41, illus. p. 49; New York, Wildenstein, 1945, *The Child Through Four Centuries*, no. 26, illus.; Cambridge, Fogg Art Museum, 1946, *Between the Empires: Géricault-Delacroix-Chasseriau, Painters of the Romantic Movement*, p. 13; SCMA, *Churchill*, 1946, illus. p. 3; Knoedler, 1953, no. 14; *University Collections*, 1956-57, no. 21, illus. p. 16; Williamstown, Massachusetts, Williams College, Lawrence Art Museum, 1960; SCMA, *Portraits*, 1962, no. 11, cover illus.; Chicago, NDC, 1964, no. 11; Poughkeepsie, New York, Vassar College Art Gallery, 1965, *Problem Pictures: Paintings Without Authors*, no. 24; Lexington, University of Kentucky Art Gallery, 1967, *Masterpieces from University Collections*, p. [16], illus. p. [23]; Middlebury [Vermont] College, 1968, *Middlebury College: A Teaching Collection*, no. 17, illus.; Colby-Currier, 1969, no. 17, illus.

REFERENCES
Churchill, 1932, p. 13, illus. no. 11; SCMA *Catalogue*, 1937, p. 20, illus. p. 83; Shoolman-Slatkin, 1942, p. 549, illus. pl. 514; SCMA, *Forty French Pictures*, 1953, no. 3, pp. iv, xxi, illus.

NOTE
This picture was purchased as a Géricault, an attribution which has not been accepted since 1953. Until the individual styles of the painters of the School of David are more clearly defined, it seems better to let the date for the *Portrait of a Youth* remain tentative, and its painter anonymous.

Albert Bierstadt
American, 1830-1902

2. *A Wilderness Lake*
1861
Oil on canvas, 25 x 39⅛ inches
Signed and dated l.l.: *ABierstadt/1861* (the A and B conjoined.)
Purchased with the assistance of funds given by Mrs. John Stewart Dalrymple (Bernice Barber '10) 1960:37

PROVENANCE
Elizabeth Tilton, Boston, to Vose Galleries, Boston, to SCMA.

EXHIBITIONS
New Bedford, 1960, no. 23; Santa Barbara Museum of Art, 1964, *Albert Bierstadt 1830-1902*, no. 18; Mount Holyoke, 1965; Colby-Currier, 1969, no. 50, illus.

REFERENCES
SCMA *Bulletin*, 1960, illus. fig. 64, pp. 64, 93; Roderick Nash, "The Cultural Significance of the American Wilderness," *Wilderness and the Quality of Life*, Maxine R. McCloskey and James P. Gilligan, eds., San Francisco, 1969, p. 71, illus. pl. 5.

Ralph Albert Blakelock
American, 1847-1919

3. *Outlet of a Mountain Lake*
c. 1887
Oil on canvas, 16 x 24 inches
Signed l.r.: *R. A. Blakelock*, in arrowhead
Purchased 1914:1

PROVENANCE
George Hearn, New York; Mrs. C. B. Smith, New York, to William Macbeth, New York, to SCMA.

EXHIBITIONS
College Art Association, *American Painting* (circulating exhibition), 1930-31; Hartford, 1935, no. 12, p. 20; Minneapolis, University of Minnesota, University Gallery, 1939, *History of American Painting*, no. 6, p. 36, illus. p. 27; Pittsburgh, Carnegie Institute, 1939, *A Century of American Landscape Painting 1800-1900*, no. 8, p. 30, illus.; New York, Whitney Museum of American Art, 1947, *Ralph Albert Blakelock Centenary Exhibition*, no. 18; Peoria, Illinois, Lakeview Center for the Arts and Sciences, 1965, *Two Hundred Years of American Painting*, p. 20, illus.; Mount Holyoke, 1965; Santa Barbara, University of California Art Galleries, 1969, *The Enigma of Ralph A. Blakelock 1847-1919*, no. 72, p. 28 [also shown in: San Francisco, Palace of the Legion of Honor, Phoenix Art Museum, and Huntington, New York, Heckscher Museum]; Colby-Currier, 1969, no. 8, illus.

REFERENCES
Churchill, 1916, p. 2; SCMA *Handbook*, 1925, p. 11, illus. p. 10; SCMA *Catalogue*, 1937, pp. 1-2, illus. p. 45.

Attributed to
Richard Parkes Bonington
English, 1801-1828

4. *View of a Norman Town*
c. 1827-28
Oil on canvas, 36 x 45 inches
Unfinished
Purchased 1952:96

PROVENANCE
Duc de Trevise(?), John Nicholson Gallery, New York, to SCMA.

EXHIBITIONS
Knoedler, 1953, no. 1; Columbus [Ohio] Gallery of Fine Arts, 1963, *Romantic Painting*, no. 3; Colby-Williams, 1966, illus.; SCMA, *Hitchcock*, 1968, no. 3, pp. 16, 21; Colby-Currier, 1969, no. 39, illus.

REFERENCES
Hitchcock, 1953, pp. 76-77, illus. p. 77; SCMA *Bulletin*, 1953, pp. 13-14, 15, illus. fig. 8; SCMA, *Forty French Pictures*, 1953, no. 10, pp. viii-ix, xv, xix, illus.; SCMA *Bulletin*, 1954-55, p. 1.

NOTE
When the Museum acquired this painting there was some question as to its attribution. Positive evidence that Bonington painted it was lacking and remains so (both Delacroix and Michel have been proposed as possible authors) but the picture seemed more important than the question of its authorship. The painting was said to have been part of the collection of the Duc de Trevise. It did not, however, appear in any of the four Trevise sales (Sotheby, July 9, 1936; Charpentier, May 19, 1938; Drouot, December 8, 1947; Charpentier, June 14, 1957).

Pierre Bonnard
French, 1867-1947

5. *Les Toits* (The roofs of the rue des Abbesses seen from the rue Tholozé)
c. 1897
Oil on cardboard, 13½ x 14½ inches
Signed and inscribed, l.r.: *Bonnard/à Paul/Bonis*
Given by the Adele R. Levy Fund, Inc. 1962:23

PROVENANCE
Paul Bonis; Dr. and Mrs. David M. Levy, New York, (1960) to Adele R. Levy Fund, Inc., New York, to SCMA.

EXHIBITIONS
MOMA, 1948, no. 6a, pp. 28, 139, illus. p. 67; New York, Museum of Modern Art, 1961, *The Mrs. Adele R. Levy Collection, a Memorial Exhibition*,

p. 22, illus.; MOMA, 1964-65, no. 7, p. 107, illus. p. 32;
London, Royal Academy of Arts, 1966, *Paintings,
Drawings, and Lithographs by Pierre Bonnard*, no. 25,
pp. 16, 36; Colby-Currier, 1969, no. 51, illus.

REFERENCES
Rewald, 1942, p. 24, illus. p. 23; Dauberville,
1965, vol. I, no. 154, p. 187, illus.

6. *Paysage du Midi*
1931
Oil on canvas, 24⅝ x 32 inches
Signed l.l. center: *Bonnard*
Purchased 1937:8

PROVENANCE
Pierre Bonnard (1931) to Bernheim-Jeune, Paris, to
Wormser (Sale, Paris, Hôtel Drouot, June 10, 1937,
no. 30, illus.); Theodore Schempp to SCMA.

EXHIBITIONS
Chicago, AIC, 1938-39, no. 22; Oberlin, Ohio, Allen
Memorial Art Museum, 1940, *Modern French Paintings*, no. 1; Andover, 1945, no. 8; MOMA, 1948, no. 61,
p. 141, illus. p. 112; Amherst, 1953; Knoedler, 1953,
no. 2; Boston, ICA, 1954, no. [1]; Wildenstein, 1955,
[French Artists] no. 3; New York, Paul Rosenberg,
1956, *A Loan Exhibition of Paintings by Pierre Bon-
nard*, no. 14, illus. p. 15; Palm Beach, Florida, The
Society of the Four Arts, 1957, *Loan Exhibition of
Works by Pierre Bonnard*, no. 19, illus.; Washington,
D.C., The Phillips Gallery, 1958, *A Loan Exhibition
of Six Paintings by Bonnard*, no. 3, illus.; Chicago,
Arts Club, 1961, no. 1 illus.; MOMA, 1964-65, no. 48,
p. 108, illus. p. 52; Munich, Haus der Kunst [in collaboration with Musée du Louvre, Paris], 1966-1967,
Pierre Bonnard, no. 109, illus.; Paris, Orangerie des
Tuileries [in collaboration with Haus der Kunst,
Munich], 1967, *Pierre Bonnard: Centenaire de sa
naissance*, no. 120, illus. [entitled, *Paysage de Normandie*]; Trenton, 1967, no. 9, illus.; Colby-Currier,
1969, no. 25, p. vii, illus.

REFERENCES
Gazette de l'Hôtel Drouot, June 1937; "Northampton: A New Ingres Drawing and a Bonnard Landscape," *Art News*, vol. XXXVI, Dec. 11, 1937, p. 17;
J[ere] A[bbott], "Other acquisitions," SCMA *Bulletin*,
1938, pp. 12-13, illus. p. 13; Abbott, 1939, p. 7, illus.;
SCMA *Catalogue Supplement*, 1941, p. 3, illus. p. 26;
Rewald, 1942, p. 24, illus. p. 25; SCMA *Bulletin*, 1947,
p. 1; SCMA, *Forty French Pictures*, 1953, no. 40, pp.
viii, xv, xix, illus.; *Apollo*, vol. 80, September 1964,
p. lvii; Dauberville, 1965, vol. III [forthcoming];
Antoine Terrasse, *Pierre Bonnard*, Paris, 1967, pp.
125-126, illus. p. 126, [entitled *Paysage de Normandie*].

Eugène Boudin
French, 1824-1898

7. *Still Life With Fish and Oysters*
c. 1854-1858
Oil on canvas, 17¾ x 29½ inches
Signed l.r.: *E. Boudin*
Purchased with the assistance of
Mrs. Henry T. Curtiss (Mina Kirstein '18) 1963:40

PROVENANCE
Private collection, Le Havre; M. Knoedler & Co.,
New York, to SCMA.

EXHIBITIONS
London, Marlborough Fine Art Limited, 1958, *Eugène
Boudin 1824-1898*, no. 92, p. 44; Colby-Currier, 1969,
no. 52, illus.

REFERENCES
Charles C. Cunningham, "Some Still-lifes by Eugène
Boudin," *Studies in the History of Art Dedicated to
William E. Suida on His Eightieth Birthday*, London,
New York, 1959, p. 385, Appendix, p. 391, no. 8;
Gazette des Beaux-Arts, Supplement no. 1141, Feb-
ruary, 1964, no. 222, p. 67, illus.

Paul Cézanne
French, 1839-1906

8. *La Route tournante à La Roche-Guyon*
c. 1885
Oil on canvas, 25¼ x 31½ inches
Purchased 1932:2

PROVENANCE
Auguste Renoir, Paris (a certificate signed by the artist's son reads: "Tableau peint par mon père et donné à Renoir, Paris le 28 Décembre, 1931."); Renou collection, Paris; Stephen Bourgeois, New York, to SCMA.

EXHIBITIONS
Chicago, AIC, 1933, no. 316, p. 46, illus.; Philadelphia, Pennsylvania Museum of Art, 1934, *Cézanne and French Painting*, no. 29, illus.; Pittsfield, Massachusetts, Berkshire Museum, 1935, *A Composition in Paint*, La Route tournante *by a Great Composer*; Toledo Museum of Art, 1936, *Cézanne-Gauguin*, no. 24, illus.; San Francisco Museum of Art, 1937, *Paul Cézanne*, illus.; New York, Paul Rosenberg, 1942, *A Loan Exhibition of Paintings by Paul Cézanne*, no. 6, p. 22, illus. p. 46; SCMA, *Churchill*, 1946, p. 6, illus. p. 8; New York, Wildenstein, 1947, *A Loan Exhibition of Cézanne*, no. 30, p. 46; Williamstown, Massachusetts, Williams College, Lawrence Art Gallery, 1948; Montreal Museum of Fine Arts, 1949, *Manet to Matisse*, no. 7; Knoedler, 1953, no. 3; Boston, ICA, 1954, no. [2]; Waterville, Maine, Colby College, 1955, *Visual Material for Creative Thinking*; Milwaukee Art Institute, 1957, *An Inaugural Exhibition: El Greco, Rembrandt, Goya, Cézanne, van Gogh, Picasso*, no. 71, illus. p. 44; New York, Wildenstein, 1959, *Cézanne*, no. 26, illus.; Chicago, Arts Club, 1961, no. 2; Colby-Currier, 1969, no. 19, p. vii, illus.

REFERENCES
Art News, vol. 30, no. 19, February 6, 1932, illus. p. 12; "Museum Accessions," *American Magazine of Art*, vol. XXIV, no. 3, March 1932, illus. p. 224; Churchill, 1932, p. 19, illus. no. 26, p. 31; Alfred Vance Churchill, "On Cézanne," *Parnassus*, vol. IV, no. V, October 1932, pp. 19-21, illus. p. 20; "Sixty-four Cézannes, Owned in America, in Exhibition," *The Art Digest*, vol. 9, no. 5, December 1, 1934, p. 6, illus.; John Rewald, *Cézanne et Zola*, Paris, 1936, illus. pl. 52; Lionello Venturi, *Cézanne, son art—son oeuvre*, Paris, 1936, vol. I, no. 441, p. 160, vol. II, illus. pl. 128; SCMA *Catalogue*, 1937, p. 13, illus. p. 70; John Rewald, *Cézanne et Zola: sa vie, son oeuvre, son amitié pour Zola*, Paris, 1939, illus. pl. 54 [reprint, with additions, of 1936 edition]; Erle Loran, *Cézanne's Composition*, Berkeley, 1943, pp. 46-47, pl. II; John Rewald, "As Cézanne Recreated Nature," *Art News*, vol. 43, no. 1, February 15-29, 1944, pp. 9-13, illus. p. 12; John Rewald, *Paul Cézanne: A Biography*, New York, 1948, p. 137, illus. no. 74; Ray Bethers, *Pictures, Painters and You*, New York, 1948, p. 104, illus. p. 105; Giovanni Scheiwiller, *Pictor Paul Cézanne*, Milan, 1950, illus. pl. IX; SCMA, *Forty French Pictures*, 1953, no. 29, pp. vii, ix-x, xiv, xix, illus.; John S. Friedenwald "Knowledge of Space Perception and the Portrayal of Depth in Painting," *College Art Journal*, vol. XV, no. 2, Winter 1955, p. 106 ff., fig. 5; George Heard Hamilton, "Cézanne, Bergson and the Image of Time," *College Art Journal*, vol. XVI, no. 1, Fall 1956, pp. 2-12, illus. p. 3; Christopher Gray, "Cézanne's Use of Perspective," *College Art Journal*, vol. XIX, no. 1, Fall 1959, pp. 54-64, illus. fig. 1, p. 55; Theodore Reff, "A New Exhibition of Cézanne," *Burlington Magazine*, vol. CII, no. 684, March 1960, p. 116; Ray Bethers, *The Language of Paintings: Form and Content*, New York, 1963, illus. p. 14; Chetham, 1969, p. 771, illus. p. 770.

James Wells Champney
American, 1843-1903

9. *Boon Companions*
1879
Oil on canvas, 17¼ x 21¼ inches
Signed and dated l.r.: *"Champ . . .'79"*
Purchased from the artist 1900:29

EXHIBITIONS
Westport [Connecticut] Community Art Association, Jesup Gallery, 1959, *Paintings of Children*, no. 8; Deerfield [Massachusetts] Academy, Hilson Gallery, *James Wells Champney*, no. 14, p. 32; Colby-Currier, 1969, p. v, no. 5, illus.

REFERENCES
Walter Montgomery, ed., *American Art and American Art Collections*, Boston, 1889, vol. II, p. 564; Churchill, 1916, p. 4; SCMA *Handbook*, 1925, p. 11; SCMA *Bulletin*, 1951, p. 30.

William Merritt Chase
American, 1849-1916

10. *Woman in Black*
c. 1881
Oil on panel, 15¼ x 9⅞ inches
Signed l.l.: *W^m. M. Chase*
Purchased from the artist 1900:16

EXHIBITIONS
Andover, Massachusetts, Addison Gallery of American Art, 1932; *American Paintings in New England Museums*; New London, Connecticut, Lyman Allyn Museum, 1945, *A Catalogue of Work In Many Media By Men of the Title Club*, no. 44; Southampton, New York, The Parrish Art Museum, 1957, *William Merritt Chase, 1849-1916, A Retrospective Exhibition*, no. 64, illus. p. 80; AFA, 1959-60; Santa Barbara, The University of California Art Galleries, 1964-65, *William Merritt Chase Retrospective*, no. 6 illus. [also

shown at: La Jolla Museum of Art, San Francisco, California Palace of the Legion of Honor, Seattle Art Museum, and New York, Gallery of Modern Art]; Colby-Currier, 1969, p. v, no. 4, illus.

REFERENCES
Churchill, 1916, p. 4; SCMA *Handbook*, 1925, p. 11; SCMA *Catalogue*, 1937, pp. 2-3, illus, p. 49; John Herron Art Museum, *Chase Centennial Exhibition*, Indianapolis, 1949, p. [76].

Jean-Baptiste Camille Corot
French, 1796-1875

11. *Jumièges*
c. 1830
Oil on canvas, 12 x 15½ inches
Signed l.l.: *COROT*
Purchased 1924:15

PROVENANCE
S.M. Vose, Providence (acquired during Corot's lifetime) to Beriah Wall, Providence (B. Wall Sale, Norman Auction Rooms, New York, November 9, 1899, no. 61) to S.M. Vose, Providence, to R.C. and N.M. Vose, Boston, to SCMA.

EXHIBITIONS
New York, Museum of Modern Art, 1930, *Corot, Daumier*, p. 6, illus. pl. 11; Chicago, AIC, 1933, no. 232, pp. 35-36; SCMA, *Corot*, 1934, no. 6, p. 21, cover illus.; Rochester Memorial Art Gallery, 1938, *The Precursors of Modern Art*, no. 5, p. 5, illus. p. 10; Wildenstein, 1943, no. 6, illus.; Williamstown, Massachusetts, Williams College, Lawrence Art Museum, 1947; Hartford, Wadsworth Atheneum, 1947, *Fifty Painters of Architecture*, no. 14, p. 25, illus. pl. VI; Detroit, 1950, no. 74, p. 41, illus. p. 40; Montreal, 1952, no. 42, illus.; Oberlin, Ohio, Allen Memorial Art Museum, 1953, *Paintings from College and University Collections*, p. 49 [catalogue in Allen Memorial Art Museum

Bulletin, vol. X, no. 2, Winter, 1953]; Knoedler, 1953, no. 5; Winnipeg, 1954, no. 37, illus. p. 21; Baltimore Museum of Art, 1954, *Man and His Years,* no. 91, p. 34; *University Collections,* 1956-57, no. 14, p. 19, illus. p. 16; Chicago, AIC, 1960, no. 25, illus.; Chicago, Arts Club, 1961, no. 5; Utica, New York, Munson-Williams-Proctor Institute and Rochester Memorial Art Gallery, *Masters of Landscape: East and West,* no. 46, illus. p. 51; Art Association of Indianapolis, Herron Museum of Art, 1965, *The Romantic Era: Birth and Flowering 1750-1850,* no. 44, color illus.; Edinburgh-London, 1965, no. 15, illus. pl. 12; Trenton, 1967, no. 14; Cobly-Currier, 1969, no. 12, illus.

REFERENCES
SCMA *Handbook,* 1925, p. 13, illus. p. 20; Alfred Vance Churchill, "Two Landscapes by Corot," SCMA *Bulletin,* 1928, pp. 7-8, illus. p. 6; Harry Adsit Bull, "The Norman Ruins of Jumièges," *International Studio,* vol. XCVIII, January 1931, p. 56, illus.; Churchill, 1932, p. 21, illus. fig. 19; " 'A Century of Progress', Chicago World Fair in Art," *London Studio,* vol. VI, no. 31, October 1933, p. 195, illus.; SCMA *Catalogue,* 1937, p. 14, illus. p. 72; SCMA, *Forty French Pictures,* 1953, no. 12, pp. vii, xiv, xix, illus.; *Art Digest,* vol. 27, no. 13, April 1953, illus. p. 14; SCMA *Bulletin,* 1953, p. 14; Faison, 1958, pp. 136-137, illus. p. 137; *Art Journal,* vol. XXIV, Spring 1965, p. 276, illus.; Chetham, 1965, p. 74, illus. p. 75.

12. *La Blonde Gasconne*
c. 1850
Oil on canvas, 15¾ x 11⅞ inches
Stamped l.l.: VENTE/COROT (Lugt 461)
Purchased 1934:7

PROVENANCE
Atelier Corot (Sale, Paris, May 26-28, 1875. no. 185) to Diot; Bonnemaison-Bascle (Sale, Paris, May 3, 1890, no. 11) to Leclanché; Bernheim-Jeune, Paris; Edouard Warneck (Sale, Paris, May 27-28, 1926, no. 91, illus. p. 114); Paul Cassirer, Amsterdam; Private collection, Holland to Alex. Reid & Lefèvre, Ltd., London, to Georges Keller, Paris, to SCMA.

EXHIBITIONS
Paris, Chambre Syndicale de la Curiosité et des Beaux-Arts, 1923, *L'Art français au service de la science française,* no. 171; Cambridge, Fogg Art Museum, 1934, *French Drawings and Paintings of the 19th Century;* London, Lefèvre, 1934, no. 12; SCMA, *Corot,* 1934, no. 12, p. 24, illus. p. 2; Cleveland Museum of Art, 1936, *20th Anniversary Exhibition,* no. 258, illus. pl. LIX; Hartford, Connecticut, Wadsworth Atheneum, 1937, *Forty-Three Portraits,* no. 36, illus.; New York, Knoedler, 1937, *Figure Pieces,* no. 5, illus.; Buffalo, Albright Art Gallery, 1938, *Picture of the Month;* Art Gallery of Toronto, 1938, *Paintings of Women from the 15th to the 20th Century,* no. 39, p. 11, illus., p. 12; Williamstown, Massachusetts, Williams College, Lawrence Art Museum, 1942; Montreal Museum of Fine Arts, 1942, *Masterpieces of Painting,* no. 53, p. 40, illus.; Philadelphia Museum of Art, 1946, *Corot, 1796-1875,* no. 23, illus.; Worcester [Massachusetts] Art Museum, 1949, *Portraits of Women, XV-XX Centuries;* The Art Gallery of Toronto, 1950, *J.B.C. Corot, 1796-1875,* no. 13; Seattle Art Museum, 1951, *Masters of Nineteenth Century Painting and Sculpture;* Knoedler, 1953, no. 6; New York, Paul Rosenberg, 1956, *Corot,* no. 17, illus. pl. 21; Chicago, AIC, 1960, no. 65, illus.; Paris, Louvre, 1962, *Figures de Corot,* no. 36, pp. 90-91, illus. p. 93; Edinburgh-London, 1965, no. 48, illus. pl. 31; Colby-Currier, 1969, no. 22, illus.

REFERENCES
Robaut, 1905, vol. 2, no. 459 *bis,* illus. p. 167, vol. 4, p. 213, no. 185; A. Bouyer, "Corot, peintre de figures," *La Revue de l'Art Ancien et Moderne,* vol. XXVI, 1909, pp. 294-306; Paul Jamot, "La 'Blonde Gasconne' de Corot," *Le Musée,* vol. VIII, 1925, pp. 50-52, pl. X;

Claude Bernheim de Villers, *Corot, peintre de figures,* Paris, 1930, no. 73, illus. p. 44; Camille Mauclair, *Corot,* Paris, 1930, illus. pl. 48; Julius Meier-Graefe, *Corot,* Berlin, 1930, p. 87; J[ere] A[bbott], "Smith College Acquires a Corot," *Art News,* vol. XXXIII, no. 3, October 20, 1934, p. 4, cover illus.; Alleyne Zander, "Individualist . . .", *Art in Australia,* November 15, 1934, pp. 54-62, illus. p. 57; "A New Corot at Smith," *American Magazine of Art,* vol. XXVII, December 1934, p. 691, illus. p. 688; "La Blonde Gasconne Added to Museum Collection," *Smith College Weekly,* October 17, 1934, p. 4, illus.; "Smith College Obtains a Classic Corot," *Art Digest,* vol. IX, no. 3, November 1, 1934, p. 9, illus.; Zervos, 1934, pp. 125-[136], illus. p. [128]; Jere Abbott," Notes on Corot," *Smith Alumnae Quarterly,* vol. XXXVI, no. 2, February 1935, p. 163, illus.; Abbott, 1935, p. 2, illus. fig. 6, p. 9; Elie Fauré, *Corot,* Paris, 1936, pl. 32; "The 20th Annual Exhibition of the Cleveland Museum of Art," *Art News,* vol. XXXIV, June 13, 1936, p. 13, illus. p. 12; scma *Catalogue,* 1937, pp. 13-14, illus. p. 73; Germain Bazin, *Corot,* Paris, 1942, p. 45, illus. p. 68; scma, *Forty French Pictures,* 1953, no. 13, pp. iv, xix, illus.; "Public Favorites," *Time,* vol. 63, May 31, 1954, p. 54, color illus. p. 55; Bernard Myers, ed., *Encyclopedia of Painting,* New York, 1955, p. 125, no. 45, illus.; Daniel Baud-Bovy, *Corot,* Geneva, 1957, p. 126; Guitar, 1959, illus. p. 113; *Art International,* vol. IX, nos. 9-10, December 20, 1965, illus. p. 26; Chetham, 1965, p. 74, illus.; Jean Leymarie, *Corot,* Geneva, 1966, p. 77, illus. p. 73; Chetham, 1969, p. 774, illus. p. 771.

NOTE

Corot painted this picture while he occupied the studio on the Quai Voltaire and retained it until his death. It appears in two versions of *L'atelier,* one in the collection of the Louvre (Robaut, 1559) and the other in the Widener Collection of the National Gallery of Art in Washington (Robaut, 1558).

13. *Dubuisson's Grove at Brunoy*
1868
Oil on canvas, 18 x 21½ inches
Signed, l.l.: *COROT*
Purchased with funds given by Miss Louise Ines Doyle ('34) 1952:116

PROVENANCE

Louis Dubuisson, Brunoy; John Nicholson Gallery, New York, to scma.

EXHIBITIONS

Knoedler, 1953, no. 7; Wellesley [Massachusetts] College, Farnsworth Museum, 1956, *Landscape Painting;* scma, *Hitchcock,* 1968, no. 5, p. 21; Colby-Currier, 1969, no. 40, illus.

REFERENCES

Robaut, 1905, vol. 3, no. 1361, p. 40, illus. p. 41; scma *Bulletin,* 1953, pp. 13, 14, 15, illus. fig. 9; Hitchcock, 1953, pp. 76-77, illus. p. 76; scma, *Forty French Pictures,* 1953, no. 14, pp. vii, xvi, xix, illus.; Faison, 1958, p. 136.

NOTE

There is another version of this picture painted for M. Latouche (Robaut,2417). Although it was commissioned as a replica of the Smith College painting, Corot changed the composition considerably and enlarged the canvas.

Gustave Courbet
French, 1819-1877

14. *La Toilette de la mariée*
c. 1858
Oil on canvas, 74 x 99 inches
Unfinished
Purchased 1929:1

PROVENANCE

Juliette Courbet, the artist's sister, (Sale, Georges Petit, Paris, July 9, 1919, no. 1) to Zoubaloff, Paris, to Paul Rosenberg & Co., Paris and New York, to SCMA.

EXHIBITIONS

Paris, Paul Rosenberg, 1924; New York, Wildenstein, 1924; Paris, Bernheim-Jeune, 1927, *Courbet*; Cambridge, Fogg Art Museum, 1929, *French Painting of the Nineteenth and Twentieth Centuries*, no. 15, illus. pl. XI; Buffalo, Albright Art Gallery, 1932, *The Nineteenth Century*, no. 11, illus. pl. VI; Chicago, AIC 1933, no. 238, p. 36, illus.; Pittsburgh, Carnegie Institute, 1936, *Survey of French Painting*, no. 15, illus. pl. XIV; SCMA, *Churchill*, 1946, p. 6; Wildenstein, 1949, no. 28, illus. p. 37; Pittsburgh, Carnegie Institute, 1951, *French Painting 1100-1900*, no. 105, illus.; *Knoedler*, 1953, no. 8; Venice, *XXVII Biennale*, 1954, no. 30, p. 155; Lyon, 1954, no. 46; London, National Gallery, Edinburgh, National Gallery of Scotland, and Manchester, City Art Gallery, 1955, *One Picture Exhibition*; Paris, Musée de l'Orangerie, 1955, *De David à Toulouse-Lautrec*, no. 11, pl. 33; Philadelphia-Boston, 1959-60, no. 50, illus.; Chicago, Arts Club, 1961, no. 6, illus.; Colby-Currier, 1969, p. vii, no. 14, illus.

REFERENCES

Guy Eglington, "An Unpublished Courbet," *International Studio*, vol. LXXIX, no. 328, September 1924, pp. 447-453, illus., with details; *Der Cicerone*, vol. XX, no. 4, February 2, 1928, illus. p. 146; *Art News*, vol. XXVII, no. 21, February 23, 1929, illus. p. 12; *Smith Alumnae Quarterly*, vol. XX, no. 2, February, 1929, illus. p. 193; "Notes of the Month," *International Studio*, vol. XCII, no. 383, April 1929, pp. 55-56, illus. p. 56; *Parnassus*, vol. I, no. V, May 1929, illus. p. 16; *Kunst und Künstler*, vol. XXVII, no. 10, July 1929, illus. p. 407; Alfred Vance Churchill, "La Toilette de la mariée by Gustave Courbet," SCMA *Bulletin*, 1929, pp. 2-21, cover illus., details pp. 6, 7,

13, 14, 17, 19, 22; Léger, 1929, p. 81, illus. pl. 37; Courthion, 1931, illus. pl. XLVII, detail pl. XLVIII; Churchill, 1932, p. 18, illus. no. 21, p. 24; Roger Fry, *Characteristics of French Art*, New York, 1933, p. 110, illus. pl. XXVI; Charles Léger, *Courbet*, Paris, 1934, no. 35, illus.; SCMA *Catalogue*, 1937, p. 16, illus. p. 78; Abbott, 1939, p. 7; SCMA *Bulletin*, 1947, p. 1; *Art Digest*, vol. 23, no. 6, December 15, 1948, p. 12, illus.; Charles Léger, *Courbet et son temps*, Paris, 1948, p. 194; Marie Louise Kaschnitz, *Gustave Courbet*, Baden-Baden, 1949, illus. pl. II; Marcel Zahar, *Gustave Courbet*, Paris, 1950, illus. pl. 38; Mack, 1951, p. 210; Roger Fry, *French, Flemish and British Art*, New York, 1951, p. 71, illus. no. 24; Pierre MacOrlan, *Courbet*, Paris, 1951, illus. no. 32; Maurice Raynal, *The Nineteenth Century: New Sources of Emotion from Goya to Gauguin*, Geneva, 1951, color illus. p. 77; Marcel Zahar, *Courbet*, Geneva, 1952, p. 122; SCMA, *Forty French Pictures*, 1953, no. 20, pp. iv, xiv, xx, illus.; Adriana Albini, *Courbet alla XXVII Biennale di Venezia*, Venice. 1954, [n.p.], illus., details; [Henry-Russell Hitchcock] "La mariée en voyage: Smith's Courbet Abroad," SCMA *Bulletin*, 1954-55, pp. 11-17; *Sele Arte*, vol. II, no. 12, May-June 1954, pp. 11-18, illus.; Sicre, 1954, vol. II, illus. p. 123; Jean Seznec, "La Mariée en voyage," *Les Amis de Gustave Courbet, Bulletin*, no. 16, 1955, pp. 7-9, cover illus.; James Thrall Soby, "Capolavori di Oltre Atlantico," *L'Illustrazione Italiana*, no. 6, June 1955, p. 48, illus. p. 49; Faison, 1958, pp. 135-36, illus. p. 134; Guitar, 1959, pp. 113-14; Douglas Cooper, "Courbet in Philadelphia and Boston," *The Burlington Magazine*, vol. CII, no. 687, June 1960, pp. 244-45; Everard M. Upjohn and John P. Sedgwick, Jr., *Highlights: An Illustrated History of Art*, New York, 1963, illus. p. 213; Eric Newton, *European Painting and Sculpture*, London, n.d. [1963] illus., detail pl. 4; Chetham, 1969, pp. 771-2, illus. p. 769.

Any discussion of *La Toilette de la mariée* must be predicated on Linda Nochlin's research on the picture for a lecture at the College on April 4, 1968, which is to be published in its entirety in the near future. In her lecture, Miss Nochlin dated the picture about 1858 and placed it in an ambitious cycle of large-scale paintings of rural and urban life which occupied Courbet in the 1850's. In the series Courbet attempted to make history painting for his own time from the events of contemporary life, as previous centuries had made it out of their own. In that, *La Toilette* is interesting since it reflects the nineteenth century concept of history as activities of ordinary people rather than rulers, treating a rural *bourgeoise* event with the scale and importance previously reserved for mythological and historical images. Furthermore, it mirrors the growing interest in the local customs of France which were threatened with extinction in the nineteenth century because of the growth of a uniform bureaucracy and industrialization.

Miss Nochlin places the iconography of the painting within the tradition of the eighteenth century *peintres gallants* which Courbet could easily have known through numerous engravings, and also in a continuing taste for the eighteenth century which was developed almost without a break by numerous *petits-maîtres* in the nineteenth century. She also discusses the "unfinished" aspects of the picture, but places the whole within an art-historical context which gives a new dimension to a picture often dismissed as "an unfinished but somehow complete formal entity."

15. *Portrait of M. Nodler, the Elder, at Trouville*
1865
Oil on canvas, 36¼ x 28¾ inches
Signed and dated l.l.:66G. /Courbet
Purchased 1935:3

PROVENANCE
M. Nodler, Paris; M. Knoedler & Co., New York, to SCMA.

EXHIBITIONS
Paris, Rond-Point du Pont de l'Alma, 1867, *Exposition des oeuvres de M. G. Courbet*, no. 78; Poughkeepsie, New York, Vassar College, 1936; Baltimore Museum of Art, 1938, *Courbet*, no. 15; Amsterdam, Stedelijk Museum, 1938, *Honderd Jaar Fransche Kunst*, no. 73, p. 54; Arts Club of Chicago, 1940, *Origins of Modern Art*, no. 5; New York, Marie Harriman Gallery, 1940, *Courbet*; Amherst [Massachusetts] College, Mead Art Building, 1948; Wildenstein, 1948-49, no. 32, illus. p. 40; Knoedler, 1953, no. 9; Venice, *XXVII Biennale*, 1954, no. 33, p. 155; Lyon, 1954, no. 36; New York, Paul Rosenberg, 1956, *Gustave Courbet*, no. 12, illus.; Philadelphia-Boston, 1959-60, no. 49, illus.; Chicago, Arts Club, 1961, no. 7; SCMA, *Portraits*, 1961, no. 14; Chicago, NDC, 1964, no. 6; The Brooklyn Museum, Richmond, Virginia Museum of Fine Arts, and San Francisco, California Palace of the Legion of Honor, 1967-68, *Triumph of Realism*, p. 23, no. 2, p. 57, illus. p. 89; Colby-Currier, 1969, no. 23, illus.

REFERENCES
Georges Riat, *Gustave Courbet, peintre*, Paris, 1906, pp. 244, 253; André Fontainas, *Courbet*, Paris, 1921, p. 71; Léger, 1929, pp. 117-128; Courthion, 1931, p. 83; J[ere] A[bbott], "A Portrait by Courbet," SCMA *Bulletin*, 1935, pp. 11-12, fig. 8; *Smith Alumnae Quarterly*, vol. XXVI, no. 4, August 1935, illus. p. 412; J[ere] A[bbott], "Smith Acquires Courbet Portrait from Knoedler," *Art News*, vol. XXXIII, no. 32, May 11, 1935, p. 1; SCMA *Catalogue*, 1937, pp. 15-16, illus. p. 76; Doris Brian, "Réalisme: G. Courbet," *Art News*, vol. XXXIX, no. 6, November 9, 1940, p. 10; *Parnassus*, vol. XII, no. 8, December 1940, illus. p. 38; SCMA *Bulletin*, 1947, p. 1; Mack, 1951, p. 211; SCMA,

Forty French Pictures, 1953, no. 21, pp. iv, xx; "A Portrait by Courbet," *Springfield Museum of Fine Arts*, [Bulletin], vol. 20, no. 3, February-March 1954; *Les Amis de Gustave Courbet, Bulletin,*no. 23, 1959, p. 9, illus. p. 11.

NOTE
Although the date on the canvas is 1866, the picture was painted in 1865. This is confirmed in a letter by Courbet to Urbain Cuénot, dated Trouville, September 16, 1865 (published in *Les Amis de Gustave Courbet,Bulletin*, no. 23, 1959). Courbet writes: "I have already done the portrait of M. Nodeler's [*sic*] son, I still have to do the ones of his brother and father, luckily I work fast." (Translation quoted from the catalogue of the Courbet exhibition held in Philadelphia and Boston, 1959-60, p. 81). The portrait of Nodler's younger brother is in the collection of the Springfield Museum of Fine Arts (illustrated in its *Bulletin*, vol. 20, no. 3, February-March, 1954).

Edgar Hilaire Germain Degas
French, 1834-1917

16. *Portrait of René de Gas (1845-1926)*
c. 1855
Oil on canvas, 36¼ x 29½ inches
Purchased 1935:12

PROVENANCE
René de Gas (Sale, Drouot, Paris, November 10, 1927, no. 72 illus.), Ambroise Vollard; M. Knoedler & Company, New York, to SCMA.

EXHIBITIONS
New York, Knoedler, 1933, *Paintings from the Ambroise Vollard Collection, XIX-XX Centuries*, no. 16, illus.; London, Lefèvre, 1934, no. 16; New York, Wildenstein, 1938, *Great Portraits from Impressionism to Modernism*, no. 7; Boston, IMA, 1939, no. 3, illus. p. 20 (also shown: New York, Wildenstein);

Cleveland Museum of Art, 1947, *Works by Edgar Degas*, no. 1, illus. pl. 1; Minneapolis Institute of Arts, 1948, *Degas' Portraits of his Family and Friends*; New York, Wildenstein, 1949, *Degas*, no. 2, illus. p. 14; Knoedler, 1953, no. 11; Detroit, 1954, no. 65, illus. p. 44; San Antonio, Marion Koogler McNay Art Institute, 1955, *Paintings, Drawings, Prints, and Sculpture by Edgar Degas*; New York, Wildenstein, 1960, *Degas*, no. 2, illus.; Chicago, Arts Club, 1961, no. 8, illus.; SCMA, *Portraits*, 1962, no. 16; Oberlin, Ohio, Allen Memorial Art Museum, 1963, *Youthful Works by Great Artists*, no. 22, illus. (Catalogue published in Allen Memorial Art Museum *Bulletin*, vol. XX, no. 3, Spring 1963); Cleveland Museum of Art, 1963, *Style, Truth and the Portrait*, no. 89, illus.; Chicago, NDC, 1964, no. 8; New Orleans, Isaac Delgado Museum of Art, 1965, *Degas in New Orleans*, illus. pl. XV, also p. 21, fig. 10; Baltimore, 1968, no. 59, p. 80, illus.; *Colby-Currier*, 1969, p. vii, no. 24, illus.

REFERENCES
Marcel Guérin, "Remarques sur des portraits de famille peints par Degas à propos d'une vente récente," *Gazette des Beaux-Arts*, vol. XVII, June 1928, p. 371; *Art News*, vol. xxxii, no. 6, November 11, 1933, illus. p. 11; "Notes of the Month: Renoir, Cézanne, and their Contemporaries at Messrs. Reid and Lefèvre's Galleries," *Apollo*, vol. 20, no. 42, July 1934, p. 42, illus.; Zervos, 1934, p. [132]; J[ere] A[bbott], "Portrait by Degas Recently Acquired by Smith College," *Art News*, vol. XXXIV, no. 12, December 21, 1935, p. 14, illus.; "College buys Degas' Portrait of Brother," *Art Digest*, vol. X, no. 7, January 1, 1936, p. 15, illus.; E. H. P[ayne], "A Newly Acquired Degas," *Smith Alumnae Quarterly*, vol. XXVII, no. 2, February 1936, pp. 161-62, illus. p. 161; "Art aux Etats-Unis—dans les musées—au Smith College Museum of Art," *Beaux-Arts*, vol. 74, n.s., no. 158, January 10, 1936, p. 4; *American Magazine*

of Art, vol. XXIX, no. 2, February 1936, illus. facing, p. 72; J[ere] A[bbott], "A Portrait of René de Gas by Edgar Degas," SCMA *Bulletin*, 1936, pp. 2-5, illus. p. 2; SCMA *Catalogue*, 1937, p. 17, illus. p. 77; Agnes Mongan, "Degas as seen in American Collections," *Burlington Magazine*, vol. LXXII, June 1938, no. 423, p. 296; Alfred M. Frankfurter, "The Sources of Modern Painting, a Concrete Exposition by the Boston Institute of Modern Art," *Art News*, vol. XXXVII, no. 24, March 11, 1939, pp. 8-14, 20, illus. p. 10; Wilenski, 1940, pp. 51, 330; Shoolman-Slatkin, 1942, p. 559, illus. pl. 544; John Rewald, *The History of Impressionism*, New York, 1946, illus. p. 50; John Rewald, "Degas and his Family in New Orleans," "*Gazette des Beaux-Arts*, series VI, vol. XXX, no. 954, 1946, pp. 105-126, illus. p. 115; Lemoisne, 1946, vol. I, p. 14, vol. II, no. 6, illus.; SCMA *Bulletin*, 1947, p. 1; "Exhibition of Portraits by Degas," *Bulletin of the Minneapolis Institute of Arts*, vol. XXXVII, no. 11, March 13, 1948, p. 54; SCMA, *Forty French Pictures*, 1953, no. 20, pp. iv, xvi, xx, illus.; Jean S. Boggs, "Degas Notebooks at the Bibliothèque Nationale," *Burlington Magazine*, vol. C, no. 662, May 1958, p. 167; Faison, 1958, p. 139, illus; Jean S. Boggs, *Portraits by Degas*, Berkeley, Los Angeles, 1962, p. 8, illus. pl. 9; Jean S. Boggs, *Drawings by Degas*, New York, 1967, p. 22; Chetham, 1969, p. 774, illus. p. 771.

NOTE

The portrait has two strips along the right and left sides. Degas began the picture on a canvas which he had already used, and x-rays show the figure of a seated woman at the left of René de Gas' head. The canvas has been exhibited sometimes with the strips showing and sometimes with them framed over.

A preliminary drawing for the portrait in the Collection of Mr. and Mrs. Paul Mellon, Upperville, Virginia, is dated 1855 (*French Paintings from the Collections of Mr. and Mrs. Paul Mellon and Mrs. Bruce Mellon*, National Gallery of Art, Washington, 1966, no. 222, illus.)

17. *Dancer on the Stage*
c. 1877-1880
Oil on canvas, 36 x 46½ inches
Stamped l.l.: *Degas* (Lugt 658)
Given by Paul Rosenberg & Co. 1955:14

PROVENANCE

Atelier Degas (Sale, Georges Petit, Paris, March 6-8, 1918, no. 27, illus.); Comte Trotti(?); Hermann Heilbuth, Copenhagen(?); Howard Young, New York; Mrs. L.L. Coburn, Chicago; Art Institute of Chicago (Coburn Bequest); Paul Rosenberg & Co., New York, to SCMA.

EXHIBITIONS

Art Institute of Chicago, 1932, *Exhibition of the Mrs. L. L. Coburn Collection, Modern Paintings and Watercolors*, no. 8; Cleveland Museum of Art, 1947, *Works by Edgar Degas*, no. 25, illus. pl. XXII; Chicago, Arts Club, 1961, no. 9; San Francisco, California Palace of the Legion of Honor, 1965, *Man: Glory, Jest, and Riddle*, no. 166, illus.; SCMA, *Hitchcock*, 1968, no. 7; Colby-Currier, 1969, no. 45, illus.

REFERENCES

Daniel Catton Rich, "Bequest of Mrs. L. L. Coburn," Art Institute of Chicago, *Bulletin*, vol. 26, no. 5, September-October 1932, pp. 66-71; Paul Lemoisne, *Degas et son oeuvre*, Paris, 1946, vol. II, no. 469, illus.; L. Browse, *Degas Dancers*, London, 1949, p. 394, illus. fig. 176; Henry-Russell Hitchcock, "A Ballet Picture by Degas," SCMA *Bulletin*, 1954-55, pp. 8-10, illus fig. 5; *Pictures on Exhibit*, vol. XVIII, no. 10, July 1955, p. 39, illus. p. 25; *Sele Arte*, vol. IV, no. 19, July-August 1955, p. 80.

NOTE

The entire left-hand side of the canvas was folded under so that only the half with the dancer was visible when the picture was in the Coburn collection. It is in its folded state that the picture is illustrated in Lemoisne.

Narcisse Virgile Diaz de la Peña
French, 1808-1876

18. *Forest Pool, Barbizon*
1862
Oil on canvas, 30 x 38¾ inches
Signed and dated l.r.: *N. Diaz 1862*
Given by Mrs. Otto Seiffert (Marjorie S. Allen '06)
1950:57

EXHIBITIONS
SCMA, *Hitchcock*, 1968, no. 8; Colby-Currier, 1969,
no. 33, illus.

REFERENCES
SCMA *Bulletin*, 1951, p. 19; SCMA, *Forty French Pic-
tures*, 1953, no. 15, pp. vii, xv, xxi, illus.; SCMA
Bulletin, 1954-55, p. 1.

Thomas Eakins
American, 1844-1916

19. *In Grandmother's Time*
1876
Signed and dated on the spinning wheel:
Eakins 76
Oil on canvas, 16 x 12 inches
Purchased from the artist 1879:1

EXHIBITIONS
Utica, New York, 1879; Burlington, University of
Vermont, Robert Hull Fleming Museum, 1933;
Springfield, Massachusetts, George Walter Vincent
Smith Art Museum, 1959, *Paintings by American
Artists: Fifty Years in Retrospect Conducted by
James D. Gill*; AFA, 1959-60; Colby-Currier, 1969,
p. v, no. 1, illus.

REFERENCES
Churchill, 1916, p. 6; SCMA *Handbook*, 1925, p. 15;
Pennsylvania Mus. *Bull.*, 1930, no. 62; Goodrich,
1933, no. 106, p. 170; SCMA *Catalogue*, 1937, p. 4,
illus. p. 51; McKinney, 1942, illus. p. 33; SCMA

Bulletin, 1951, p. 29; *Art News*, vol. 56, no. 4, Summer, 1957, p. 43, illus.; Chetham, 1965, p. 74, illus.
p. 75; Chetham, 1969, p. 769, illus. p. 768.

20. *Portrait of Mrs. Edith Mahon*
1904
Oil on canvas, 20 x 16 inches
Inscribed on the back: *To My Friend Edith Mahon/
Thomas Eakins, 1904*
Purchased 1931:2

PROVENANCE
Edith Mahon to Pancoast Galleries, Wellesley, to
SCMA.

EXHIBITIONS
Knoedler, New York, 1944, *Thomas Eakins Cen-
tennial*, no. 74, illus.; Utica, New York, Munson
Williams Proctor Institute, 1947, *Homer-Eakins*;
Wellesley, 1949-50; Williams, 1950; New York,
Wildenstein, 1952, *Seventy Twentieth Century
American Paintings*, no. 62; Providence, Museum
of Art of the Rhode Island School of Design, 1952,
Sculpture by Painters; Knoedler, 1953, no. 35;
Pomona, California, Los Angeles County Fair, 1953,
Painting in the USA 1721-1953; Chapel Hill, Univer-
sity of North Carolina, William Hayes Ackland
Memorial Art Center, 1958, *Paintings, Drawings,
Prints and Sculpture from American College and
University Collections*, no. 109, illus.; Williams, 1960;
Chicago, Arts Club, 1961, no. 10; Washington,
National Gallery of Art, Art Institute of Chicago, and
Philadelphia Museum of Art, 1961-1962, *Thomas
Eakins: A Retrospective Exhibition*, no. 93, illus.
p. 126; SCMA, *Portraits*, 1962, no. 19, cover illus.;
SCMA, *American Painting*, 1964, no. 17, illus.; Balti-
more, 1968, no. 64, p. 85, illus.; New York, Portraits,
Inc., 1968, *Portraits of Yesterday and Today*; Colby-
Currier, 1969, no. 16, illus.

REFERENCES

Pennsylvania Mus. *Bull.*, 1930, no. 256; Goodrich, 1933, no. 407, p. 199, illus. pl. 63; SCMA *Catalogue*, 1937, p. 4, illus. p. 52; McKinney, 1942, illus. p. 39; Larkin, 1949, p. 278, illus.; SCMA *Bulletin*, 1951, pp. 29, 31; SCMA *Bulletin*, 1954-55, p. 4; Faison, 1958, pp. 139-40, illus. p. 139; Guitar, 1959, illus. p. 115; Samuel M. Green, *American Art: A Historical Survey*, New York, 1966, p. 410; Sylvan Schendler, *Eakins*, Boston, 1967, p. [226] illus. no. 113; Novak, 1969, p. 210, illus. p. 209.

NOTE

Edith Mahon was an English pianist who came to this country sometime before 1900. She was a friend of the Eakins, and often played for the painter in the evenings in his studio. The portrait was not commissioned but was painted as a gift. Mrs. Mahon died in 1923 or 1924, having returned to England. In a letter of April 27, 1931, the painter's widow wrote to Alfred Vance Churchill that she knew, not from the lady herself but from outside sources, that Edith Mahon had suffered much from unkindness.

Edwin Romanzo Elmer
American, 1850-1923

21. *Mourning Picture*
c. 1889
Oil on canvas, 28 x 36 inches
Purchased 1953:129

PROVENANCE

Maud Valona Elmer (the artist's niece), Greenfield, Massachusetts, to SCMA.

EXHIBITIONS

SCMA, 1952 *Edwin Romanzo Elmer: 1850-1923*, no. 4; Frankfurt, Städelsches Kunstinstitut, Munich, Bayerische Staatsgemäldesammlungen, and Hamburg, Kunsthalle, 1953, *Hundert Jahre amerikanische Malerei*, no. 29, p. 23, illus. no. 25 [also shown in: Berlin, Charlottenburger Schloss, Düsseldorf, Kunstammlungen der Stadt, 1953, Rome, Gallerie Nazionale d'Arte Moderna, 1954, *Pittura Americana del XIX Secolo*, no. 72, Milan, Palazzetto Reale, and New York, Whitney Museum of American Art, 1954, *American Painting in the Nineteenth Century*, no. 71, on checklist]; Houston, Museum of Fine Arts, 1956, *American Primitive Art*, no. 2, illus.; Brussels, *Universal and International Exhibition*, 1958, *American Art*, no. 102, p. 52; Rotterdam, Museum Boymans-van Beuningen, and Paris, Musée National d'Art Moderne, 1964, *De Lusthof der Naïeven*, no. 58, illus., with detail [catalogue also published in Paris: *Le Monde des naïfs*]; New York, Whitney Museum of American Art, 1966, *Art of the United States*, no. 90, p. 149, illus. p. 37; Colby-Currier, 1969, no. 42, illus.

REFERENCES

SCMA *Bulletin*, 1951, pp. 30-31, p. 34; Alfred Frankenstein, "Edwin Romanzo Elmer," *Magazine of Art*, vol. 45, no. 6, October 1952, pp. 270-272, illus. p. 271; *Antiques*, vol. LXIV, no. 2, August 1953, illus. p. 124; John I.H. Baur, *American Painting in the Nineteenth Century*, New York, 1953, p. 22, illus. p. 53; Frankenstein, 1953, p. 151; SCMA *Bulletin*, 1954-55, p. 41; John Maass, *The Gingerbread Age*, New York, 1957, illus. p. 190; Oto Bihalji-Merin, *Das naive Bild der Welt*, Cologne, 1959, p. 89, illus. pp. 198-9; Gillo Dorfles, "L'arte dei 'primitivi-contemporanei'," *Domus*, no. 379, June 1961, pp. 53-54, illus., detail, p. 53; Maud V. Elmer, "Edwin Romanzo Elmer as I Knew Him," *Massachusetts Review*, vol. I, no. 1, Autumn-Winter, 1964-65, pp. [121-144], illus. pp. [132-33], detail, p. [134]; J. W. Schulte Nordholt, *Amerika: Land, Volk, Kultur*, Baarn, 1965, illus. no. 23b; *Encyclopedia of World Art*, New York, Toronto, 1966, vol. XI, p. 715, illus. pl. 334; Lloyd Goodrich, "American Art and the Whitney Museum," *Antiques*, vol. XC, no. 5, November 1966, illus. p. 659.

NOTE

Elmer's *Mourning Picture* was painted in the spring of 1889 soon after the death of his daughter Effie Lillian, who is pictured in the foreground with her pets and toys. Maud Elmer, the niece of the artist, said that Effie was painted with a lamb to show that she was dead (the Lamb of God was a popular device for children's tombs in New England), but also said the child had a pet lamb as well. In her reminiscences, Miss Elmer wrote "At Grandfather Whiting's, my father told me that Effie was dead. It was unbelievable until my aunt Susie cut a white Calla lily from her house plants, tied it with ferns, and my father took me across the road where I placed it on the still form of my playmate. Then I knew." (Maud Valona Elmer, *op. cit.*, p. [136]). In the background of the painting, the dead child's parents, the artist and his wife Mary Jane Ware Elmer, are depicted seated in front of the house which Elmer and his brother had built for themselves and their parents at Shelburne Falls, Massachusetts in 1876. The house is still standing.

Henri Fantin-Latour
French, 1836-1904

22. Portrait of Mr. Becker
1886
Oil on canvas, 40 x 32½ inches
Signed and dated u.l.: *Fantin '86*
Purchased 1964:33

PROVENANCE

Mr. Becker, Springfield, Ohio; Amédée Pigeon, Paris; Ferdinand and Julien Tempelaere, Paris; Henri Darasse, Paris; Hector Brame, Paris; Alex. Reid and Lefèvre, Ltd., London; E.J. van Wisselingh Co., Amsterdam; C.R.A. van Stolk, Bergen, N.H., The Netherlands, to SCMA.

EXHIBITIONS

Paris, Palais de l'Ecole Nationale des Beaux-Arts, 1906, *Exposition de l'oeuvre de Fantin-Latour*, no. 58; Musée de Grenoble, 1936, *Centenaire de Henri Fantin-Latour*, no. 38; Amsterdam, E.J. van Wisselingh, 1938, *Maitres français du XIXme et XXme siècle*, no. 16; New York, Scott and Fowles, 1951, *Spring Show of Fantin-Latour: Flowers, Fruits, and Figures*; SCMA, 1966, *Henri Fantin-Latour*, no. 20, illus.; Colby-Currier, 1969, no. 54, illus.

REFERENCES

Adolphe Jullien, *Fantin-Latour, sa vie et ses amitiés*, Paris, 1909, p. 205; Mme. Fantin-Latour, *Catalogue de l'oeuvre complet de Fantin-Latour*, Paris, 1911, no. 1253; *Art News Annual—Annual Christmas Edition*, 1958, p. 169; Chetham, 1969, p. 775.

NOTE

According to Mme. Fantin, the model for *Portrait de Mme. X.* [Mme. Fantin-Latour, *op. cit.*, 1196] prevailed upon Fantin to paint her portrait even though he had refused once. At the first sitting she insisted upon paying 5,000 francs, saying that since Fantin did not know her, she felt she must. This annoyed the artist, but he was obliged to accept. During the sittings Mme. X., or Mme. Leroy as she came to be known, was particularly gracious to the artist and his wife. The day the picture was finished "Mme. Leroy" (Fantin was convinced this was not her real name) took the painting away with her in a cab. An American named Mr. Becker accompanied her for the sittings and during the course of the meetings also sat for his own portrait. While Mr. Becker was in no way mysterious he provided no information about Mme. Leroy. Some years later the American painter Frank Boggs (1855-1927), who had lived in Paris since he was 20, saw the portrait of Mr. Becker at Hector Brame's and identified it as his uncle's.

Paul Gauguin
French, 1848-1903

23. *Banlieue Parisienne*
1879
Oil on canvas, 26 x 39 inches
Signed l.l.: *P. Gauguin 79*
Purchased 1953:55

PROVENANCE
Ambroise Vollard, Paris; Etienne Bignou, Paris;
E.J. van Wisselingh & Co., Amsterdam; Vose Gal-
leries, Boston, to SCMA.

EXHIBITIONS
SCMA, *Nineteenth Century Paintings Supplementing
the Permanent Collection*, (Commencement Exhibition), 1953; Boston, ICA, 1954, no. [7]; New York, The
Solomon R. Guggenheim Museum, 1966, *Gauguin and
the Decorative Style*, no. [1]; SCMA, *Hitchcock*, no. 10,
p. 22; Colby-Currier, 1969, no. 41, illus.

REFERENCES
Maurice Malingue, *Gauguin: Le Peintre et son oeuvre*,
Paris, 1948, illus. pl. 77; *Art Quarterly*, vol. XVI,
no. 3, Autumn, 1953, illus. p. 270; Henri Dorra, "A
Suburban Landscape by Gauguin," SCMA *Bulletin*,
1953, pp. 2-4, fig. 1; SCMA *Bulletin*, 1954-55, p. 1;
Faison, 1958, p. 138, illus.

Anne-Louis Girodet de Roucy-Trioson
French, 1767-1824

24. *Portrait of Madame Benoit-François Trioson(?)*
1804
Oil on canvas, 25½ x 21⅜ inches
Signed and dated 1804 with the painter's mono-
gram l.r.
Purchased with the assistance of the Eleanor Lamont
Cunningham, ('32) Fund 1956:19

PROVENANCE
Wildenstein and Company, New York, to SCMA.

EXHIBITIONS
South Hadley, Massachusetts, Dwight Art Memorial,
Mount Holyoke College, 1966, *The Legacy of David
and Ingres to Nineteenth Century Art*, no. 23; Colby-
Currier, 1969, no. 47, illus.

REFERENCES
George Levitine, "A New Portrait by Girodet," *Art
Quarterly*, vol. XIX, no. 4, Winter 1956, pp. 435-436,
illus. p. 432; *Sele Arte*, vol. V, no. 26, September-
October 1956, p. 64, illus.; *Arts*, vol. 31, no. 3, December 1956, illus. p. 17; Robert O. Parks, "About
the Cover," *Smith Alumnae Quarterly*, vol. XLVIII,
no. 2, Winter 1957, p. 73, cover illus.; George Levitine,
"A New Portrait by Girodet," SCMA *Bulletin*, 1957,
pp. 16-20, illus. p. 16; Musée de Montargis, 1967,
Girodet: Exposition du deuxième centenaire, listed in
the chronology for 1804.

Juan Gris
Spanish, 1887-1927

25. *Still Life: The Bottle of Rum*
c. 1914
Oil on canvas, 13⅝ x 8⅝ inches
Signed on the back of the canvas: *Juan Gris*
Given by Joseph Brummer 1923:2-2

EXHIBITIONS
Chicago, Arts Club, 1939, no. 21, illus.; Wellesley,
1949-1950; Troy, New York, The Emma Willard
School, 1960, *Emma Willard Alumnae Association
Exhibition to Celebrate the Opening of the New Arts
Center*; Colby-Currier, 1969, no. 11, illus.

REFERENCES
SCMA *Catalogue*, 1937, p. 30.

26. *Fruit Dish and Bottle*
1916
Oil on canvas, oval, 25⅝ x 31⅞ inches
Signed and dated l.l.: *Juan Gris 3.1916*
Given by Joseph Brummer 1921:8-4

EXHIBITIONS
Cambridge, Fogg Art Museum, 1937; Bennington
[Vermont] College, 1938; Chicago, Arts Club, 1939,
no. 2; New York, Buchholz Gallery, 1947, *Paintings by
Juan Gris*; Cincinnati, Modern Art Society, 1948,
A Retrospective Exhibition of the Work of Juan Gris,
no. 16; Dartmouth, 1950; Boston, ICA, 1954, no. [8];
Berkeley, University of California Art Gallery, 1960,
Art from Ingres to Pollock, p. 52; Chicago, Arts Club,
1961, no. 12; Wolfsburg, Stadhalle, 1961, *Franzö-
sische Malerei von Delacroix bis Picasso*, no. 78, illus.
pl. 75; Cambridge, Fogg Art Museum, extended loan,
1963-1969; Colby-Currier, 1969, no. 10, illus.

REFERENCES
SCMA *Handbook*, 1925, p. 19; SCMA *Catalogue*, 1937,
p. 29, illus. p. 102; SCMA, *Forty French Pictures*, 1953,
no. 38, pp. x, xiii, xxii, illus.

Childe Hassam
American, 1859-1935

27. *Union Square in Spring*
1896
Oil on canvas, 21½ x 21 inches
Signed and dated l.r.: *Childe Hassam 1896*
Purchased 1905:3

PROVENANCE
Childe Hassam to SCMA through Montross Galleries,
New York.

EXHIBITIONS
New York, Walker Galleries, 1939, *Views of New
York*; Cambridge, Fogg Art Museum, 1941, *American
Landscape Painting: George Inness to George Bellows*,
no. 15; Charlotte, North Carolina, The Mint Museum
of Art, 1946, *Tenth Anniversary Exhibition*, no. 3;
Dayton Art Institute and Columbus [Ohio] Gallery of
Fine Arts, 1951, *America and Impressionism*;
Amherst, 1953; Boston, ICA, 1954, no. [10]; Mount
Holyoke, 1956, no. 35, p. [6]; Amherst, Jones
Library, 1958; Washington, Corcoran Gallery of
Art, Boston, Museum of Fine Arts, Manchester, New
Hampshire, Currier Gallery of Art, and New York,
Gallery of Modern Art, 1965, *Childe Hassam, a
Retrospective Exhibition*, no. 23, illus. p. 27; New
York, Jewish Museum, 1967, *The Lower East
Side: Portal to American Life (1870-1924)*, no. 22;
Colby-Currier, 1969, no. 6, illus.

REFERENCES
Childe Hassam, *Three Cities*, 1899, illus.; Churchill,
1916, p. 8; SCMA, *Handbook*, 1925, p. 21, illus.
p. 34; SCMA, *Catalogue*, 1937, p. 6, illus. p. 56;
J. A. Kouwenhoven, *Columbia Historical Portrait of
New York*, New York, 1953, p. 17, illus.; Burne Ho-
garth, "Outline of American Painting: Painters of
Modernism and Reality, The Ten, The Eight, The
Armory Show (1900-1930)," *American Artist*, vol. 26,
no. 4, issue 254, April 1962, illus. p. [65]; Henry C.
Pitz, "The Turning Wheel," *American Artist*, vol. 28,
no. 3, issue 273, March 1964, illus. p. 28; John Pearce,
American Painting, New York, 1964, p. 48, (illus.,
color slide no. 24).

Winslow Homer
American, 1836-1910

28. *Shipbuilding at Gloucester*
1871
Oil on canvas, 13½ x 19¾ inches
Signed and dated, l.l.: *HOMER 71*
Purchased 1950:99

PROVENANCE
M. Knoedler & Co., New York, (c. 1945) to Joseph Katz, Baltimore, to Victor Spark, New York, to SCMA.

EXHIBITIONS
SCMA and Williamstown, Massachusetts, Williams College, Lawrence Art Museum, 1951, *Winslow Homer: Illustrator*, no. 22, illus.; Knoedler, 1953, no. 36; Syracuse, 1953, no. 17, illus. p. 8; Middletown, Connecticut, Wesleyan University, Davison Art Center, 1954; Richmond, Virginia Museum of Fine Arts and Newport News, Mariner's Museum, 1964, *Homer and the Sea*, no. 2, illus.; SCMA, *American Painting*, 1964, no. 12; SCMA, *Hitchcock*, 1968, no. 11, illus. p. 26; Colby-Currier, 1969, no. 6, illus.

REFERENCES
SCMA *Bulletin*, 1951, p. 30, illus. fig. 14; SCMA *Bulletin*, 1954-55; p. 4; Lloyd Goodrich, "Homer and the Sea," *Arts in Virginia*, vol. 5, no. 1, Fall 1964, pp. 12-21, illus. p. 13.

NOTE
Like many of Homer's early paintings, this composition formed the basis of a wood engraving published in *Harper's Weekly*, October 11, 1873, where a group of boys was added in the foreground.

William Morris Hunt
American, 1824-1879

29. *Portrait of William Sidney Thayer*
c. 1860
Oil on canvas, 21⅞ x 18 inches
Given by Miss Sarah S. Thayer 1900:8

EXHIBITIONS
Williams, 1950; Colby-Currier, 1969, no. 3, illus.

REFERENCES
Churchill, 1916, p. 9; SCMA *Handbook*, 1925, p. 21; SCMA *Catalogue*, 1937, p. 7.

NOTE
There is another version of the portrait in the collection of one of Thayer's collateral descendants, and it has not been determined which of the two pictures is the first version and which the replica, although both are almost certainly by Hunt. Miss Sarah Thayer lived in Northampton and presented the portrait of her brother to the Hillyer Art Gallery in 1897 or 1898.

Jean Auguste Dominique Ingres
French, 1780-1867

30. *The Death of Leonardo da Vinci*
c. 1818
Oil on canvas, 16⅜ x 19¼ inches
Purchased 1950:98

PROVENANCE
Atelier Ingres (Sale, Drouot, Paris, April 27, 1867, lot 10) to Goldber; Mme. Ingres (Sale, Drouot, Paris, April 10, 1894, lot 59); Baron Vitta (Sale, Drouot, Paris, June 27-28, 1924, lot 57) to Vaudoyer (Anonymous Sale, June 23, 1925, lot 42) to Sholing; J. B. Neumann (Sale, Rains Auction Rooms, New York, January 24, 1936, lot 61, illus.) to Julius H. Weitzner, New York; E. and A. Silberman Galleries, New York (1936-1950), to SCMA.

EXHIBITIONS

Paris, Association Franco-Américaine, Hôtel de la Chambre Syndicale de la Curiosité et des Beaux-Arts, 1921, *Exposition Ingres*, no. 221; Dallas Museum of Fine Arts, 1936, *Catalogue of the Exhibition of Paintings, Sculptures and Graphic Arts*, Eighteenth Century Room, no. 10, p. 28; Flint [Michigan] Institute of Arts, [1941], *Six Centuries of Painting*, no. 16; illus.; Shreveport, The Louisiana State Exhibition Building, 1949, *Five Centuries of Art*; Poughkeepsie, New York, Vassar College Art Gallery, 1952, *French Paintings*; Knoedler, 1953, no. 20; Andover, Massachusetts, Addison Gallery of American Art, 1954, *Variations, Three Centuries of Painting*, no. 4; New York, E. and A. Silberman Galleries, 1957, *Art Unites Nations*, no. 14, illus.; London, Tate Gallery, 1959, *The Romantic Movement*, no. 221; Colby-Williams, 1966; SCMA, *Hitchcock*, 1968, no. 12, p. 22; Colby-Currier, 1969, p. vii, no. 35, illus.

REFERENCES

L. Hourticq, *Ingres*, Paris, 1928, p. iv; Jerome Klein, "An Unpublished Painting from the Studio of Ingres," *Burlington Magazine*, vol. LVII, September, 1930, pp. 136-141, illus. pl. IB; J.B. Neumann, ed., *Living Art: Chardin-Rouault*, n.d., n.p., illus.; SCMA *Bulletin*, 1951, pp. 18-19; SCMA, *Forty French Pictures*, 1953, no. 5, pp. iv, xvi, xxiii, illus.; Georges Wildenstein, *Ingres*, New York, 1954, p. 188, no. 119, fig. 66; Keith Andrews, *The Nazarenes: A Brotherhood of German Painters in Rome*, Oxford, 1964, p. 133, illus. pl. 80b.

NOTE

This picture is the first of two replicas of a painting commissioned in 1818 by the Comte de Blacas, French Ambassador in Rome, as a pendant to *Henri IV Playing With His Children* (Wildenstein, *op. cit.*, no. 113) of 1817 which was also in his collection. Both pictures were acquired by the Petit Palais, Paris, from the Marquise de Virier, née de Blacas, in 1968. The Smith canvas remained unknown to the literature until it was published by Jerome Klein (*op. cit.*) in 1930. The second version, painted about 1851 for Alexander von Humboldt, was sold in 1969 (Sotheby's, 30 April 1969, lot 20, color illus. opp. p. 39).

Ernst Ludwig Kirchner
German, 1880-1938

31. *Dodo and Her Brother*
c. 1908
Oil on canvas, 67⅛ x 37⁷⁄₁₆ inches
Signed l.l.: *E. L. Kirchner*
Purchased 1955:59

PROVENANCE

Kirchner Estate (the back of the canvas bears the stamp: *Nachlass E. L. Kirchner*, with the notation: *Dre/Ba 10*), to Galerie Beyeler, Basel, to E. and A. Silberman Galleries, New York, to SCMA.

EXHIBITIONS

St. Gallen, Kunstmuseum, 1950, *E.L. Kirchner*, no. 5; Basel, Galerie Beyeler, 1955, *Expressionisten*, no. 16, illus.; New York, Museum of Modern Art and City Art Museum of St. Louis, 1957-58, *German Art of the Twentieth Century* [cat. ed. by Andrew C. Ritchie], no. 70, p. 221, illus. p. 39; Cleveland, 1960, no. 14, pp. 21-22, illus. p. 11; Chicago, Arts Club, 1961, no. 13, illus.; SCMA, *Portraits*, 1961, no. 20; Wellesley [Massachusetts] College, Jewett Arts Center, 1963, *Painting and Sculpture in Europe and America from 1900-1914*; New York, The Solomon R. Guggenheim Museum, 1964, *Van Gogh and Expressionism*; New York, PEA, 1966, no. 72, illus. p. 51; Amherst [Massachusetts] College, Mead Art Building, 1966, *German Art After World War I*; Seattle Art Museum, Pasadena Art Museum and Boston, Museum of Fine Arts,

1968-69, *Ernst Ludwig Kirchner: A Retrospective Exhibition* [catalogue by Donald E. Gordon], no. 11, illus. pp. 18,44; Colby-Currier, 1969, no. 46, illus.

REFERENCES
Lothar-Günther Buchheim, *Die Künstlergemeinschaft Brücke*, Feldafing, 1956, illus. fig. 158; *Art News*, vol. 55, no. 3, May 1956, cover illus. in color; Robert O. Parks, "A Note on the Cover Painting," *College Art Journal*, vol. XV, no. 3, Spring 1956, p. 184, cover illus.; *Art Quarterly*, vol. XIX, no. 2, Summer 1956, p. 206, illus. p. 204; *Sele Arte*, vol. V, no. 26, September-October 1956, illus. p. 64; Robert O. Parks, "Smith College Collects Plus," *Smith Alumnae Quarterly*, vol. XLVII, no. 2, Winter 1956, p. 86, illus. p. 87; Bernard S. Myers, "Kirchner's Dodo and her Brother," SCMA *Bulletin*, 1957, pp. 21-26, illus. fig. 10, p. 22; Peter Seltz, *German Expressionist Painting*, Berkeley, 1957, p. 103, color illus. pl. 147; Guitar, 1959, pp. 114, 115, color illus. p. 112; Enrico Crispolti, *Ernst Kirchner* (I Maestri del Colore), Milan, 1966, color illus. pl. IV; Donald E. Gordon, "Kirchner in Dresden," *Art Bulletin*, vol. XLVIII, nos. 3-4, 1966, p. 346, illus. fig. 25; Edward Bryant, "The Boom in U. S. University Museums," *Art News*, vol. 66, no. 5, September 1967, pp. 30-47, color illus. p. 44; Donald E. Gordon, *Ernst Ludwig Kirchner*, Cambridge, 1968, pp. 58, 70, 272, no. 48, illus. pl. 13; *Encyclopaedia Britannica*, Chicago, 1970, vol. 15, illus. p. 630C.

NOTE
The painting came to the Museum entitled *Erich Heckel and His Wife*. However, a letter from Erich Heckel dated November 21, 1956, now in the archives of the Museum, states that the picture ". . . does not represent me and Frau Heckel whom I did not even know at the time the picture was painted, but Kirchner's friend and model, Dodo, and her brother."

Franz Kline
American, 1910-1962

32. *Rose, Purple and Black*
1958
Oil on canvas, 45 x 36 inches
Signed and dated on reverse: *Franz Kline 1958*
Given by Mr. and Mrs. Sigmund W. Kunstadter (Maxine Weil '24) 1965:27

PROVENANCE
Sidney Janis Gallery, New York (1959), to Mr. and Mrs. Sigmund W. Kunstadter, Highland Park, Illinois, to SCMA.

EXHIBITIONS
New York, Museum of Modern Art, International Council, Traveling Exhibition, 1963-64, *Franz Kline*, shown in: Amsterdam, Stedelijk Museum, (no. 40 in catalogue), Turin, Galleria Civica d'Arte Moderna, Brussels, Palais des Beaux-Arts, Basel, Kunsthalle, London, Whitechapel Gallery, Vienna, Museum des 20. Jahrhunderts, and Paris, Musée National d'Art Moderne; Boston, Institute of Contemporary Art and Pittsfield, Massachusetts, Berkshire Museum, 1967, *New Directions in Collecting: Part One, Museum Acquisitions*, no. 24; Amherst, 1968; Colby-Currier, 1969, p. vii, no. 56, illus.

REFERENCES
Chetham, 1969, p. 775.

Fernand Léger
French, 1881-1955

33. *Elément mécanique I*
1924
Oil on canvas, 25½ x 20 inches
Signed and dated, l.r.: *F.LEGER .24*
Purchased 1954:75

PROVENANCE
John Quinn, New York; Nierendorf Gallery, New York, to G. David Thompson, Philadelphia, to Curt Valentin Gallery, New York, to SCMA.

EXHIBITIONS
Poughkeepsie, New York, Vassar College Art Gallery, 1965, *Art Since 1923*, no. 13; SCMA, *Hitchcock*, 1968, no. 13, p. 22, illus. p. 14; Colby-Currier, 1969, no. 44, illus.

REFERENCES
SCMA *Bulletin*, 1954-55, p. 1, illus. p. 3; *Art Journal*, vol. XXIV, no. 4, Summer 1965, cover illus.

Edouard Manet
French, 1832-1883

34. *Portrait of Marguérite de Conflans*
1873
Oil on canvas, 21 x 17½ inches
Signed and dated, l.l.: *Manet/1873*
Purchased 1945:6

PROVENANCE
Atelier Manet (no. 53) to Ignace Ephrussi, Paris, to Alexandre Rosenberg, Paris, (1898) to H.O. Havemeyer, New York, (Sale, Anderson Galleries, New York, April 10, 1930, no. 73) to Paul Rosenberg, New York, to SCMA.

EXHIBITIONS
New York, Durand-Ruel, 1913, *Loan Exhibition of Paintings by Edouard Manet*, no. 11; New York, Durand-Ruel, *The Four Great Impressionists*, 1940, no. 11, illus.; Boston, Institute of Modern Art, 1943, *French Art of the Nineties*; Richmond, Virginia Museum of Fine Arts, 1944, *19th Century French Paintings*, no. 12, illus.; New London, Connecticut, Lyman Allyn Museum, 1950, *From Delacroix to the Neo-Impressionists*; Amherst, 1953; Knoedler, 1953, no. 21; Boston, ICA, 1954, no. [13]; New York, Paul Rosenberg, 1957, *Masterpieces Recalled*, no. 9, illus.; Boston, Institute of Contemporary Art, 1960, *The Image Lost and Found*, no. 3, illus.; SCMA, *Portraits*, 1962, no. 15; New York, Wildenstein, and Waltham, Massachusetts, Brandeis University, Rose Art Museum, 1962, *Modern French Painting*, no. 30, illus.; Chicago, NDC, 1964, no. 18; Philadelphia Museum of Art and Art Institute of Chicago, 1966-1967, *Manet*, no. 121, illus., detail, p. 137; Colby-Currier, 1969, no. 31, illus.

REFERENCES
Théodore Duret, *Histoire d'Edouard Manet et de son oeuvre, avec un catalogue des peintures et des pastels*, Paris, 1902, 1919, no. 156; Théodore Duret, *Manet and the French Impressionists*, London, 1910, no. 156, p. 234; Julius Meier-Graefe, *Edouard Manet*, Munich, 1912, illus. fig. 160; Etienne Moreau-Nélaton, *Manet raconté par lui-même*, Paris, 1926, vol. II, no. 81, pp. 33, 129, illus. fig. 207 facing p. 32; Adolphe Tabarant, "Les Manets de la collection Havemeyer," *La Renaissance*, vol. XIII, no. 2, February 1930, p. 72, illus. p. 67; Adolphe Tabarant, *Manet, Histoire catalographique*, Paris, 1931, no. 208; Paul Jamot and Georges Wildenstein, *Manet*, Paris, 1932, vol. I, no. 236, illus. fig. 84; Robert Rey, *Manet*, New York, 1938, illus. p. 64; Elizabeth McCausland "Exhibitions in New York," *Parnassus*, vol. XII, no. 4, April 1940,

illus. p. 37; Adolphe Tabarant, *Manet et ses oeuvres*, Paris, 1947, pp. 224-225, illus. fig. 212; Hartt, 1947, pp. 3-6, cover illus. in color; SCMA, *Forty French Pictures*, 1953, no. 28, pp. iv, xiv, xxiii, illus.; Faison, 1958, pp. 139-140, illus. p. 139.

Alfred Henry Maurer
American, 1868-1932

35. *Le Bal Bullier*
c. 1904
Oil on canvas, 28⅝ x 36⅛
Signed l.r.: *Alfred H. Maurer*
Purchased 1951:283

PROVENANCE
René Lefebvre, Paris; Paul Clemens, Milwaukee; M. Knoedler & Co., New York, to SCMA.

EXHIBITIONS
Milwaukee, Walker Art Center and New York, Whitney Museum of American Art, 1949, *A.H. Maurer: 1868-1932*, no. 10, [also shown: Boston, Institute of Contemporary Art]; Knoedler, 1953, no. 38; Boston, ICA, 1954 no. [15]; Williamstown, Massachusetts, Williams College, Lawrence Art Museum, 1954; Amherst [Massachusetts] College, Mead Art Building, 1956, *20th Century American Painting*; South Hadley, Massachusetts, Mount Holyoke College, Dwight Art Memorial, 1957, *Twenty-five Years of Alfred Maurer*, no. 1; Amherst, Jones Library, 1958; Durham, University of New Hampshire, Paul Art Center, 1960, *Art in New England Colleges*, no. 23; SCMA, *Hitchcock*, 1968, no. 15, p. 24, illus. p. 27; Colby-Currier, 1969, no. 37, illus.

REFERENCES
SCMA *Bulletin*, 1953, p. 25, illus. fig. 17; Elizabeth McCausland, *A.H. Maurer*, New York, 1951, pp. 70, 78, 95; John I.H. Baur, ed. *New Art in America*, New York, 1957, illus. p. 177.

Georges Michel
French, 1763-1843

36. *Landscape*
Oil on paper, mounted on canvas, 10½ x 14 inches
Signed l.r.: *G. M.*
Purchased 1919:2

PROVENANCE
Alfred Vance Churchill, Northampton, to SCMA.

EXHIBITIONS
Middletown, Connecticut, Wesleyan University, 1931; Detroit, 1950, no. 79, p. 42; Colby-Currier, 1969, no. 9, illus.

REFERENCES
SCMA *Handbook*, 1925, p. 25; SCMA *Catalogue*, 1937, p. 22, illus. p. 87.

Jean-François Millet
French, 1814-1875

37. *Portrait of William Morris Hunt*
c. 1853-55
Signed u.r.: *J.F.M.*
Oil on canvas, 22 x 18 inches
Purchased 1951:291

PROVENANCE
Duz, Paris, (Anonymous Sale, April 6, 1888, referred to in Widener catalogue) to Féral, to P.A.B. Widener, Philadelphia; Victor Spark, New York, to SCMA.

EXHIBITIONS
Knoedler, 1953, no. 22; Williams, 1960; SCMA *Portraits*, 1962, no. 13; Milwaukee Art Center, 1966, *The Inner Circle*, no. 67, illus.; SCMA, *Hitchcock*, 1968, no. 16, p. 24; Colby-Currier, 1969, no. 38, illus.

REFERENCES
Louis Soullié, *Les grands peintres aux ventes publiques II: Peintures, aquarelles, pastels, dessins de*

Jean-François Millet, Paris, 1900, p. 70; Widener
Coll., 1915, no. 42, illus.; SCMA *Bulletin*, 1953, pp. 13,
16, illus. fig. 7; SCMA, *Forty French Pictures*, 1953,
no. 16, pp. iv, xxiii, illus.

38. *Farm at Gréville*
c. 1871
Oil on canvas, 21¼ x 28⅝ inches
Signed l.l.: *J. F. Millet*
Purchased 1931:10

PROVENANCE
J. Blakeslee (1893) to P.A.B. Widener, Philadelphia;
M. Knoedler & Co., New York, to SCMA.

EXHIBITIONS
University of Rochester, Memorial Art Gallery, *The
Development of Landscape Painting through Twenty
Centuries of European Art*, 1934, no. 39, p. 9; Middletown, Connecticut, Wesleyan University, *Millet*,
1938; Deerfield [Massachusetts] Academy, *The Loan
of the Week*, (October 18-31), 1944; SCMA, *Churchill*,
1946, pp. 5-6; Detroit, 1950, no. 109, p. 54, illus.
p. 53; Art Gallery of Toronto, 1950, *Fifty Paintings
by Old Masters*, no. 26; Knoedler, 1953, no. 23;
Winnipeg, 1954, no. 46, illus. p. 22; Chicago, Arts
Club, 1961, no. 14; Colby-Currier, 1969, no. 18, illus.

REFERENCES
Widener Coll., 1915, no. 43, illus.; Churchill, 1932,
p. 34, illus. p. 23; SCMA *Catalogue*, 1937, p. 22, illus.
p. 89; Hans Tietze, *Masterpieces of European Painting
in America*, New York, 1939, no. 275, p. 328, illus.
p. 275; SCMA *Bulletin*, 1951, p. 19; SCMA *Forty French
Pictures*, 1953, no. 17, pp. vii, x, xxiii, illus.

Claude Monet
French, 1840-1926

39. *The Seine at Bougival*
1869

Oil on canvas, 28½ x 23½ inches
Signed l.r.: *Claude Monet*
Purchased 1946:4

PROVENANCE
Depeaux, Paris; Charles Viguier, Paris; Sir William
van Horne, Montreal; M. Knoedler & Co., New York,
to SCMA.

EXHIBITIONS
Art Association of Montreal, 1933, *Selection of Paintings from the Collection of the Late Sir William van
Horne*; Manchester, New Hampshire, Currier Gallery
of Art, 1949, *Monet and the Beginnings of Impressionism*, no. 39; Knoedler, 1953, no. 24; Boston ICA,
1954, no. [17]; Edinburgh, Royal Scottish Academy,
and London, Tate Gallery, 1957, *Claude Monet*, no.
15, illus. pl. 2; Montreal Museum of Fine Arts, 1960,
Canada Collects: European Painting, no. 74, illus.
p. 31; Chicago, Arts Club, 1961, no. 15; Colby-
Currier, 1969, p. vii, no. 32, illus.

REFERENCES
Hartt, 1947, pp. 6-8, illus. p. 6, detail, p. 7; SCMA,
Forty French Pictures, no. 26, pp. vii, xiv, xxiii, illus.;
Chetham, 1969, p. 774, illus. p. 772.

40. *Field of Poppies*
1890
Oil on canvas, 23½ x 39½ inches
Signed and dated l.r.: *Claude Monet 90*
Given by Honorable and Mrs. Irwin Untermeyer
1940:10

PROVENANCE
Durand-Ruel, New York, to Samuel Untermeyer,
New York, (Sale, Parke-Bernet, New York, May 10,
1940, no. 21, illus.) to Honorable and Mrs. Irwin
Untermeyer, New York, to SCMA.

EXHIBITIONS

New York, Metropolitan Museum, 1907; Andover, 1945, no. 16; Boston, ICA, 1954, no. [18]; Mount Holyoke, 1956, no. 15, p. [4]; St. Louis, City Art Museum and Minneapolis Institute of Arts, 1957, *Claude Monet*, no. 74; Claremont, California, Pomona College, 1967, *Impressionism*, no. 11; Colby-Currier, 1969, no. 29, illus.

REFERENCES

"Northampton: Landscape by Monet for College," *Art News*, vol. XXXIX, no. 10, December 7, 1940, p. 14; Jere Abbott, "Champ de Coquelicots," SCMA *Bulletin*, 1941, p. 10, illus. fig. 4; SCMA *Catalogue Supplement*, 1941, pp. 4-5, illus. p. 27; SCMA, *Forty French Pictures*, 1953, no. 27, pp. xiv, xxiii, illus.

41. *Cathedral at Rouen*
1894
Oil on canvas, 36½ x 29¹⁄₁₆ inches
Signed and dated l.r.: *Claude Monet '94*
Given by Miss Caroline R. Wing ('96) and Miss Adeline F. Wing ('98) 1956:24

PROVENANCE

Durand-Ruel, Paris; Mme. van Nierup, Paris; M. Knoedler & Co., New York, to SCMA.

EXHIBITIONS

Colby-Currier, 1969, no. 48, illus.

REFERENCES

Helen Comstock, "The Connoisseur in America," *Connoisseur*, vol. CXXXVIII, no. 556, November 1956, p. 143, illus.; *Sele Arte*, vol. V, no. 26, September-October 1956, p. 64, illus.; Faison, 1958, pp. 137-138, illus. p. 137; SCMA *Bulletin*, 1958, illus. fig. 35.

Giorgio Morandi
Italian, 1890-1964

42. *Still Life*
1954
Oil on canvas, 14 x 18¼ inches
Signed l.l.: *Morandi*
Purchased from the artist 1954:62

EXHIBITIONS

Deerfield [Massachusetts] Academy, 1956, *Contemporary Italian Art*; Providence, Museum of Art of the Rhode Island School of Design, 1967, *Seven Centuries of Italian Art*; Cambridge, Massachusetts, Busch-Reisinger Museum, 1968, *Works by Giorgio Morandi*, no. 7, cover illus.; SCMA, *Hitchcock*, 1968, no. 17, p. 24; Colby-Currier, 1969, no. 43, illus.

John Frederick Peto
American, 1854-1907

43. *Discarded Treasures*
c. 1904
Oil on canvas, 22 x 40 inches
Falsely signed l.l. with monogram initial: *HARNETT*
Purchased 1939:4

PROVENANCE

Earle's Galleries, Philadelphia; The Downtown Gallery, New York, to SCMA.

EXHIBITIONS

New York, The Downtown Gallery, 1939, *"Nature-Vivre," by William M. Harnett*, no. 11, cover illus.; Pittsburgh, Carnegie Institute, 1940, *Survey of American Painting*, no. 129; New York, The Downtown Gallery, 1948, *Harnett 100th Anniversary*; Sarasota, John and Mable Ringling Museum of Art, 1949, *Survey of American Art of the 18th and 19th Centuries*; SCMA, The Brooklyn Museum and San Francisco, California Palace of the Legion of Honor, 1950, *John F. Peto*, no. 47, p. 27, illus. fig. 21; Wesleyan, 1951, no. 7; Williamstown, Massachusetts, Williams College, Lawrence Art Museum, 1953, *American*

"Fool-the-Eye" Still Life; Knoedler, 1953, no. 40; Syracuse, 1953, no. 22; Boston, ICA, 1954, no. [21]; Philadelphia, Pennsylvania Academy of Fine Arts, 1955, *One Hundred and Fiftieth Anniversary Exhibition*, no. 178, [also shown: Madrid, La Dirección General de Bellas Artes, Florence, Palazzo Strozzi, Innsbruck, Tiroler Landesmuseum Ferdinandeum, Ghent, Musée Vander Haeghen, and Stockholm, Kungl. Akademien för de Fria Konsterna]; Chicago, Arts Club, 1961, no. 17, cover illus.; Dallas Museum of Contemporary Arts, 1961, *The Art that Broke the Looking Glass*, no. 69, illus. p. 54; SCMA, *American Painting*, 1964, no. 16, illus.; Minneapolis, 1963-64, illus.; University of Rochester, Memorial Art Gallery, 1964-65 *In Focus: A Look at Realism in Art*, no. 55, illus.; La Jolla Museum of Art and Santa Barbara Museum of Art, 1965, *The Reminiscent Object: Paintings by William Harnett, John F. Peto and John Haberle*, no. 48, illus.; New York, PEA, 1966, no. 45, illus. p. 37; Colby-Currier, 1969, no. 27, illus.

REFERENCES
M[ary] B[est], "Discarded Treasures by William Harnett," SCMA *Bulletin*, 1939, pp. 17-19, illus. p. 18; *American Magazine of Art*, vol. 32, no. 5, May 1939, illus. p. 315; *Smith Alumnae Quarterly*, vol. XXXI, no. 1, November, 1939, illus. p. 27; James W. Lane, "This Year the Carnegie National, Pittsburgh's Brilliant Survey of 160 years of U.S. Painting," *Art News*, vol. XXXIX, no. 4, October 26, 1940, p. 16, illus. p. 12; SCMA *Catalogue Supplement*, 1941, p. 4, illus. p. 20; Dorothy C. Miller, "Discovery and Rediscovery," *Art in America*, vol. XXXIII, no. 4, October 1945, pp. 255-260, illus. p. 256; Alfred Frankenstein, "Harnett, True and False," *Art Bulletin*, vol. XXXI, no. 1, March 1949, pp. 38-56, illus. fig. 2; Lloyd Goodrich, "Harnett and Peto: A Note on Style," *Art Bulletin*, vol. XXXI, no. 1, March 1949, pp. 57-58, illus. fig. 2; Frankenstein, 1953, pp. 5, 16, 17, 47, 107, 110, 111, 176, illus. pl. 17; Sicre, 1954, vol. II, illus. p. 124; SCMA *Bulletin*, 1954-55, p. 4; Faison, 1958, p. 137, illus.

NOTE
At the time this painting was purchased, the Harnett signature was thought to be authentic, and the picture was exhibited and published as a Harnett until 1949. Alfred Frankenstein's article in the *Art Bulletin* (*op. cit.*) established beyond doubt that the signature is false, and in the same issue, Lloyd Goodrich's stylistic analysis showed that the painting is the work of Peto.

Pablo Picasso
Spanish, 1881-

44. *La Table*
1919-1920
Oil on canvas, 50 x 29½ inches
Signed l.r.: *Picasso*
Purchased 1932:15

PROVENANCE
Valentine Dudensing Gallery, New York, to SCMA.

EXHIBITIONS
Hartford, Wadsworth Atheneum, 1934, *Picasso*, no. 36, illus.; New York, Museum of Modern Art, 1936, *Cubism and Abstract Art*, no. 224, p. 221, illus. fig. 78; Toledo Museum of Art, 1938, *Contemporary Movements in European Painting*, no. 87; New York, Museum of Modern Art, 1939, *Picasso, Forty Years of his Art*, no. 147, p. 101, illus. p. 100; Worcester [Massachusetts] Art Museum, 1941, *The Art of the Third Republic: French Painting 1870-1940*, no. 35, illus.; Mexico City, Sociedad de Arte Moderno, 1944, *Picasso*, p. 41, illus. p. [55]; Cambridge, Fogg Art Museum, 1947; Sarasota, Florida, The John and Mable Ringling Museum of Art, 1948, *Masterpieces of Modern Painting*, p. [19], illus. p. [18]; Art Gallery of Toronto and Montreal Museum of Fine Arts, 1949, *Works by Picasso*, no. 10; Hartford, Wadsworth

Atheneum, 1952, *Wadsworth Atheneum: 110 Years,
An Exhibition Reviewing the History of the Wads-
worth Atheneum, 1842-1952*; Knoedler, 1953, no. 25;
Boston, ICA, 1954 no. [27]; Wildenstein, 1955, [French
Artists] no. 22; New York, Gallery "G," 1955, *The
Eye of man: Form and Content in Modern Art*, no. 3;
Wesleyan, 1958; Cleveland, 1960, no. 21, p. 25, illus.
p. 13; Chicago, Arts Club, 1961, no. 18, illus.; New
York, Paul Rosenberg, 1962, *Picasso: An American
Tribute, The Twenties*, no. 12; Colby-Currier, 1969,
p. vii, no. 20, illus.

REFERENCES
W.B. Rogers, *A Picture Is A Picture: A Look at Modern Painting*, New York, 1924, p. 82, illus.; William
Gaunt, "Picasso and the *cul-de-sac* of Modern Painting," *Atelier*, vol. I, April 1931, pp. 408-416, illus.
p. 415; "Museum Accessions," *American Magazine
of Art*, vol. XXVI, no. 4, April 1933, p. 213, illus. p.
208; J[ere] A[bbott], "An Abstract Painting by Picasso," SCMA *Bulletin*, 1933, pp. 2-6, illus. p. 2 (re-
printed in SCMA *Bulletin*, 1954-55, pp. 29-34); Helen
Gardner, *Art Through the Ages*, rev. ed. New York,
1936, p. 727, illus. p. 724; George E. Diller and Ramon
Guthrie, eds., *French Literature and Thought Since
the Revolution*, New York, 1942, illus. opp. p. 513;
Alfred H. Barr, Jr., *Picasso: Fifty Years of His Art*,
New York, 1946, p. 112, illus. p. 113; SCMA *Bulletin*,
1947, p. 1; Zervos, 1949, vol. III, no. 437, illus. pl.
146; Katherine Kuh, *Art Has Many Faces: The Nature of Art Presented Visually*, New York, 1951,
p. 122, illus. p. 123, fig. 196; SCMA, *Forty French Pictures*, 1953, no. 39, pp. x-xi, xiv, xv, xxiii, illus.;
Faison, 1958, p. 141, illus.; Guitar, 1959, p. 114, illus.
p. 113; Chetham, 1965, p. 75, illus.; Alan Gowans,
*Restless Art: A History of Painters and Painting,
1760-1960*, Philadelphia, New York, 1966, illus. fig.
35B; Chetham, 1969, p. 774, illus. p. 770.

45. *Les Misérables (Les Pauvres au bord de la mer)*
1903
Oil on canvas, 23½ x 19½ inches
Signed u.r.: *Picasso*
Given by Jere Abbott 1965:33

PROVENANCE
Joseph Stransky, New York, to Wildenstein and
Company, New York, to Jere Abbott, to SCMA.

EXHIBITIONS
Hartford, Wadsworth Atheneum, 1933, *Literature
and Poetry in Painting since 1850*; SCMA, 1966, *A New
Picasso for Smith College*; Colby-Currier, 1969,
no. 44, illus.

REFERENCES
Zervos, 1949, vol. I, no. 197, illus. pl. 89; Pierre Daix
and Georges Boudaille, *Picasso, The Blue and Rose
Periods: A Catalogue Raisonné of the Paintings
1900-1906*, Paris, 1966, p. 220, color illus. p. 217;
Priscilla Paine van der Poel, "Picasso's Les Misérables," *Smith Alumnae Quarterly*, vol. LVII, no. 3,
Spring 1966, pp. 140-142, illus., cover, p. 140;
"Picasso's Les Misérables," *Burlington Magazine*,
vol. CVIII, no. 762, September 1966, p. 483, illus.
p. 482; *Art Journal*, vol. XXV, no. 4, Summer 1966,
cover illus.; *Gazette des Beaux-Arts*, Supplement
no. 1176, February 1967, no. 373, p. 106, illus.;
Chetham, 1969, p. 775; André Fermigier, *Picasso*,
Paris, 1969, illus. p. 40, fig. 22.

William Matthew Prior
American, 1806-1873

46. *Mount Vernon and the Tomb of Washington*
c. 1855
Oil on canvas, 18¾ x 28¾ inches
Stencil on reverse: *PAINTING GARRET/NO 36
TRENTON STREET/EAST BOSTON/W. M.
PRIOR.*
Purchased 1950:72

EXHIBITIONS
Amherst, Jones Library, 1958; Colby-Currier, 1969, no. 34, illus.

REFERENCES
SCMA *Bulletin*, 1951, p. 34.

NOTE
Found under a print in an old frame purchased from an antique shop near Plymouth, Massachusetts (1950).

Pierre Auguste Renoir
French, 1841-1919

47. *Portrait of Mme. Edouard Maître*
c. 1871
Oil on canvas, 14¾ x 12¾ inches
Signed u.l.: *Renoir*
Purchased 1924:16

PROVENANCE
Cassirer; Dikran Kélékian, New York, (Sale, American Art Association, New York, January 30-31, 1922, no. 103, illus.) to Stephen Bourgeois, New York, to SCMA.

EXHIBITIONS
Buffalo, Albright Art Gallery, 1930, *Commemoration of the Twenty-fifth Anniversary of the Opening of the Albright Art Gallery*, no. 58; Milwaukee, Downer College, 1938, *Renoir's Paintings*; San Francisco, California Palace of the Legion of Honor, 1944, *Paintings by Pierre Auguste Renoir*, illus. p. 16; New York, Wildenstein, 1950, *Auguste Renoir*, no. 5, illus. p. 35; SCMA, *Churchill*, p. 6, illus. p. 8; Knoedler, 1953, no. 26; Detroit, 1954, no. 60; Los Angeles County Museum and San Francisco Museum of Art, 1955, *Renoir*, no. 7; Montclair [New Jersey] Art Museum, 1957, *Master Painters*, no. 36; SCMA, *Portraits*, 1962, no. 18, cover illus.; Chicago, NDC, 1964, no. 24; Colby-Currier, 1969, no. 13, illus.

REFERENCES
Collection Kélékian: Tableaux de l'école française moderne, Paris, 1920, illus. pl. 54; SCMA *Handbook*, 1925, p. 27, illus. p. 46; Julius Meier-Graefe, *Renoir*, Leipzig, 1929, no. 25, illus. p. 40; Churchill, 1932, p. 29, illus. no. 25; Albert C. Barnes and Violette de Mazia, *The Art of Renoir*, New York, 1935, no. 22; SCMA *Catalogue*, 1937, p. 23, illus. p. 90; Wilenski, 1940, pp. 61, 339; SCMA, *Forty French Pictures*, 1953, no. 25, pp. iv, xiv, xxiv, illus.

NOTE
Madame Maître was the wife of Edouard Maître, the musician and close friend of Renoir, Bazille and other painters in the 60's and 70's of the last century. Maître appears in the Fantin-Latour painting, *A Studio in the Batignolles Quarter*, 1870, Louvre, and in the Bazille, *The Artist's Studio, rue de la Condamine*, 1870, Louvre. A second portrait of Madame Maître, by Fantin-Latour, is now in The Brooklyn Museum.

Anton Romako
Austrian, 1832-1889

48. *Girl on a Swing* (Olga Wassermann, 1872-1944)
c. 1882
Oil on canvas, 63 x 48 inches
Signed l.l.: *A. Romako*
Purchased 1963:58

PROVENANCE
Anna Wassermann (the sitter's daughter), Lucerne, to Galerie St. Etienne, New York, to SCMA.

EXHIBITIONS
Chicago, NDC, 1964, no. 25; Portland [Oregon] Art Museum, 1967, *75 Masterworks: An Exhibition of Paintings in Honor of the Seventy-fifth Anniversary of the Portland Art Association, 1892-1967*, no. 14, illus.; Colby-Currier, 1969, no. 53, illus.

REFERENCES

Fritz Novotny, *Der Maler Anton Romako*, Vienna, 1954, pp. 56, 63, no. 314; *Gazette des Beaux-Arts*, Supplement, no. 1141, February 1964, illus. p. 70, no. 230; Chetham, 1969, p. 775.

NOTE

The subject of the painting is Olga Wassermann (1872-1944). Her father, August Wassermann, an honorary citizen of the United States, was instrumental in negotiating and signing the treaty whereby the United States acquired Alaska from Russia. Olga was born in San Francisco on the return journey of one of her parents' trips to Alaska. When her father retired to Paris in the 1880's he summoned Romako from Vienna to do several family portraits. A portrait of August Wassermann, painted a few years earlier in Hungary, is now in the Museum of Fine Arts, Budapest. Olga Wassermann married Max Wassermann, one of Berlin's leading bankers and the brother of the famous biologist.

Henri Rousseau
French, 1844-1910

49. *Banks of the Oise*
1905
Oil on canvas, 18 x 22 inches
Signed l.l.: *H. Rousseau*
Purchased 1939:7

PROVENANCE

Dr. Blank, Hofheim im Taunus (1914); Suermondt, Drove (1921-26); A. M. Voemel, Düsseldorf (1927); Berthold Nothmann, Berlin, to Marie Harriman Gallery, New York, to SCMA.

EXHIBITIONS

Paris, Salon des Indépendants, 1906, no. 4368; Berlin, Galerie Flechtheim, 1926, *Henri Rousseau*; Art Institute of Chicago and New York, Museum of Modern Art, 1942, *Henri Rousseau*, pp. 39, 44, illus. p. 42; Pittsburgh, Carnegie Institute, 1942, *Henri Rousseau*, no. 2; Wildenstein, 1948, no. 39, illus. p. 53; Cincinnati Art Museum, 1951, *Paintings 1900-1925*, no. 5; Boston, ICA, 1954, no. [24]; Chicago, Arts Club, 1961, no. 21; New York, Wildenstein, 1963, *Henri Rousseau*, no. 41, illus.; New York, The Solomon R. Guggenheim Museum, 1968, *Rousseau, Redon and Fantasy*, no. [6]; Colby-Currier, 1969, no. 28, illus.

REFERENCES

Wilhelm Uhde, *Henri Rousseau*, Düsseldorf, 1914, p. 64, illus.; Wilhelm Uhde, *Henri Rousseau*, Dresden, 1921, p. 47, illus. p. 48; Roch Grey, *Henri Rousseau*, Rome, 1922, illus. pl. [13]; Adolphe Basler, *Henri Rousseau et son oeuvre*, Paris, 1927, illus. pl. XXVI; Philippe Soupault, *Henri Rousseau, le Douanier*, Paris, [1927], illus., pl. [18]; André Salmon, *Henri Rousseau dit le Douanier*, Paris, 1927, illus. pl. 23; Christian Zervos, *Rousseau*, Paris, 1927, illus. pl. 92 b; Adolphe Basler, *H. Rousseau*, Paris, 1929, illus. pl. 47; "Northampton: A Rousseau Acquisition," *Art News*, vol. XXXVIII, no. 3, October 21, 1939, p. 14, illus.; *Smith Alumnae Quarterly*, vol. XXXI, no. 1, November 1939, p. 27, illus.; J[ere] A[bbott], "Bords de l'Oise," SCMA *Bulletin*, 1940, pp. 17-19, illus. fig. 10, p. 18; SCMA *Catalogue Supplement*, 1941, p. 6, illus. p. 30; Cheney, 1941, illus. p. 367; J[ohn] O'C[onnor], "Henri Rousseau," *Carnegie Magazine*, vol. XVI, no. 7, December 1942, pp. 209-213; Shoolman-Slatkin, 1942, p. 563, pl. 565; Roch Grey, *Henri Rousseau*, Paris, [1943], illus. pl. 48; Daniel Catton Rich, *Henri Rousseau*, New York, 1946, pp. 44, 46, illus. p. 42; SCMA *Bulletin*, 1947, p. 1; SCMA, *Forty French Pictures*, no. 34, pp. vii, xiv, illus.; Sicre, 1954, vol. II, illus. p. 125; Faison, 1958, p. 137 illus.; Guitar, 1959, illus. p. 115; Jean Bouret, *Henri Rousseau*, New York, 1961, no. 159, pp. 37, 259, illus. p. 218; Dora Vallier, *Henri Rousseau*, Paris,

1961, pp. 305, 313, color illus. p. [85]; Giovanni Artieri and Dora Vallier, *L'opera completa di Rousseau il Doganiere*, (Classici dell'Arte, 29) Milan, 1969, no. 173, pp. 85, 102, color illus. pl. XXXII.

Pierre Etienne Théodore Rousseau
French, 1812-1867

50. *The Bridge at Moret*
c. 1828-1829
Oil on canvas, 10½ x 13¼ inches
Stamped l.l.: *TH.R* (Lugt 2436)
Purchased 1957:32

PROVENANCE
Auguste Rousseau (Sale, Georges Petit, Paris, March 9, 1900, no. 41, p. 59, illus.); Vicomte de Turel, Paris; K. Rosenthal, Paris; Dr. Willi Raeber, Basel, to SCMA.

EXHIBITIONS
Toledo Museum of Art, San Francisco, California Palace of the Legion of Honor, Cleveland Museum of Art, and Boston, Museum of Fine Arts, 1962-1963, *Barbizon Revisited* no. 82; Colby-Currier, 1969, no. 49, illus.

REFERENCES
Art Quarterly, vol. XX, no. 4, Winter 1957, p. 474, illus.; Germain Bazin, "Théodore Rousseau," *Connaissance des Arts*, no. 189, November 1967, pp. 94-99, color illus. p. 94; Leopold Reidemeister, "L'Ile-de-France et ses peintres," *L'Oeil*, no. 124, April 1965, pp. 15-21, illus. p. 18.

Albert Pinkham Ryder
American, 1847-1917

51. *Perrette*
c. 1890
Oil on canvas, mounted on wood,
12¾ x 7⅝ inches

Signed l.l.: *A. P. Ryder*
Purchased from the artist 1893:1

EXHIBITIONS
New York, Metropolitan Museum of Art, 1918, *A Loan Exhibition of the Works of Albert P. Ryder*, no. 14, pl. 14; Hartford, 1935, no. 30; New York, Knoedler, 1939, *Two American Romantics of the Nineteenth Century: Robert Loftin Newman (1827-1912) Albert Pinkham Ryder (1847-1917)*, no. 15; New York, Whitney Museum of American Art, 1947, *Albert P. Ryder Centenary Exhibition*, no. 29, p. 45; Knoedler, 1953, no. 42; Syracuse, 1953, no. 22; New Bedford, 1960, no. 7, pl. 7; Chicago, Arts Club, 1961, no. 22; Washington, D.C., Corcoran Gallery of Art, 1961, *Albert Pinkham Ryder*, no. 32, illus. p. 34; Colby-Currier, 1969, no. 2, illus.

REFERENCES
Churchill, 1916, p. 12; Frederic Fairchild Sherman, *Albert Pinkham Ryder*, privately printed, New York, 1920, no. 117, p. 72; Frederic Newlin Price, *Ryder*, New York, 1932, no. 133; SCMA *Handbook*, 1925, p. 27, illus. p. 48; SCMA *Catalogue*, 1937, p. 8, illus. p. 60; James W. Lane, "A View of Two Native Romantics," *Art News*, vol. XXXVIII, no. 6, November 11, 1939, p. 9; Lloyd Goodrich, *Albert P. Ryder*, New York, 1959, no. 55, p. 115, illus. pl. 55.

John Singer Sargent
American, 1856-1925

52. *My Dining Room* (Broadway, Worcestershire)
c. 1889
Oil on canvas, 29 x 23¾ inches
Purchased from funds given by
Mrs. Henry T. Curtiss (Mina Kirstein '18)
in memory of William Allan Neilson 1968:10

PROVENANCE
Wilfred G. de Glehn, London (1926, with Mrs.

de Glehn, 1955); Wildenstein and Company, New York, to SCMA.

EXHIBITIONS
London, Chenil Galleries, 1925; Liverpool, Walker Art Gallery, 1925, *Fifty-third Autumn Exhibition (Including a Collective Exhibit of Work by the Late John S. Sargent, R.A.)*, no. 138, p. 20; London, Royal Academy, 1926, *Exhibition of Works by the Late John S. Sargent, R.A.*, no. 333, p. 50; SCMA, 1968, *My Dining Room and Preparatory Sketches and a Drawing for the Murals in the Boston Public Library by John Singer Sargent*; Colby-Currier, 1969, no. 58, illus.

REFERENCES
J.B. Manson, "Notes on the Works of J.S. Sargent," *The Studio*, vol. XC ,no. 389, August 15, 1925, pp. 78-87, illus. p. 83; Evan Charteris, *John Sargent*, London, 1927, pp. 115, 287; Charles Merrill Mount, *John Singer Sargent: A Biography*, New York, 1955, p. 446, no. K8710; Charles Merrill Mount, *John Singer Sargent: A Biography*, London, 1957, p. 356, no. K8710; *Gazette des Beaux-Arts*, Supplement, no. 1201, February 1969, no. 328, illus. p. 81.

NOTE
The three pictures in the long horizontal frame, seen in the background of this painting, were identified by David McKibbin as sketches of the painter, Paul Helleu, who visited the Sargents at Fladbury Rectory near Broadway on his wedding trip in 1889. The three studies, a drawing and two watercolors, were once in the collection of Sargent's sister, Emily. (The Frick Art Reference Library has a photograph of the three sketches in the original frame). In 1950, Mrs. Francis Ormond (Violet Sargent) gave the drawing which appears in the center of the frame, to the Metropolitan Museum. One of the watercolors is still in the collection of Sargent's niece, Mrs. Hugo Pitman.

Georges Seurat
French, 1859-1891

53. *Woman with a Monkey*
1884
Oil on wood, 9¾ x 6¼ inches
Purchased 1934:2-1

PROVENANCE
Jean Ajalbert; Gaston Bernheim de Villers, Paris; Etienne Bignou, Paris; Galerie Barbazanges, Paris, to M. Knoedler & Co., New York, to Mr. and Mrs. Cornelius J. Sullivan, New York; Mrs. Cornelius J. Sullivan, New York, to SCMA.

EXHIBITIONS
London, Knoedler, 1926, *Modern French Painters*, no. 19; New York, Knoedler, 1927, *The Last Fifty Years in French Art*, no. 15; New York, Museum of Modern Art, 1929, *First Loan Exhibition: Cézanne, Gauguin, Seurat, van Gogh*, no. 65, illus.; London, Alex. Reid & Lefèvre, Ltd., 1930, *Renoir and the Post Impressionists*; Springfield [Massachusetts] Museum of Art, 1933, *Inaugural Exhibition*, no. 136; The Renaissance Society of the University of Chicago, 1935, *Twenty-four Paintings and Drawings by Georges-Pierre Seurat: Studies for La Grande Jatte and Other Pictures*, no. 5, illus.; New London, Connecticut, Lyman Allyn Museum, 1937; Wildenstein, 1943, no. 22; Wildenstein, 1948, no. 49, illus. p. 62; New York, Knoedler, 1949, *Seurat, Paintings and Drawings*, no. 15, illus.; Providence, Museum of Art, Rhode Island School of Design, 1951, *Paris: Many Happy Returns! An Exhibition in Honor of the 2,000th Anniversary of the Founding of the City of Paris*, no. [24]; Montreal, 1952, no. 62, illus.; Knoedler, 1953, no. 30; New York, Wildenstein, 1953, *Seurat and His Friends*, no. 7, illus. p. 23; Boston, ICA, 1954, no. [25]; Cambridge, Fogg Art Museum, 1955, *From Sisley to Signac*, no. 26; Houston, Contemporary Arts Museum, 1956, *Shadow and Substance: The Shadow Theatre of Montmartre and Modern Art*; Art Institute of Chicago and New York, Museum of

Modern Art, 1958, *Seurat: Paintings and Drawings*,
no. 86, illus. p. 63; Chicago, Arts Club, 1961, no. 23;
New York, The Solomon R. Guggenheim Museum,
1968, *Neo-Impressionism*, no. 74, p. 109, illus.;
Colby-Currier, 1969, no. 21, illus.

REFERENCES
Christian Zervos, "Un Dimanche à la Grande Jatte
et la technique de Seurat," *Cahiers d'Art*, vol. 9, no. 9,
1928, pp. 361-375, illus. p. 375; *Parnassus*, vol. VI,
no. 4, April 1934, illus. pl. 19; "Seurat for Smith College Museum," *American Magazine of Art*, vol.
XXVII, no. 5, May 1934, p. 279, illus.; *Smith Alumnae
Quarterly*, vol. XXV, no. 3, May 1934, p. 265; J[ere]
A[bbott], "Woman with a Monkey," scma *Bulletin*,
1934, pp. 12-13, illus., p. 13; Daniel Catton Rich,
Seurat and the Evolution of "La Grande Jatte," Chicago, 1935, p. 23, no. 31, p. 55, illus. pl. xxx; scma
Catalogue, 1937, p. 24, illus. p. 91; Abbott, 1939, p.
20; John Rewald, *Georges Seurat*, New York, 1943,
1946, illus. fig. 69, p. 97; Parker Tyler, "The Hu-
manism of Abstract Art," *Gazette des Beaux-Arts*,
6th ser. vol. XXXI, 1947, pp. 47-60, illus. p. 57; scma
Bulletin, 1947, p. 1; John Rewald, *Seurat*, Paris, 1948,
p. 59, illus. pl. 44; Jacques de Laprade, *Seurat*, Paris,
[1951], illus. p. 44; scma, *Forty French Pictures*, 1953,
no. 32, pp. iv, vi, xiv, xxiv, illus.; John Rewald, *Post-
Impressionism from van Gogh to Gauguin*, New
York, 1956, illus. p. 85; Leslie Katz, "Seurat: Allegory
and Image," *Arts*, vol. 32, no. 7, April 1958, pp.
40-47, illus. p. 47; Faison, 1958, p. 136; Henri Dorra
and John Rewald, *Seurat*, Paris, 1959, no. 134, p. 145,
illus.; François Mathey, *Les Impressionistes et leurs
temps*, Paris, 1959, color illus. p. 117; César M. de
Hauke, *Seurat et son oeuvre*, Paris, 1961, vol. I, no.
137, p. 88, illus. p. 89; Renata Negri, "Seurat e il
divisionismo," *L'Arte Moderna*, vol. 1, no. 5, 1967,
color illus. p. 170; Pierre Courthion, *Georges Seurat*,
New York, 1968, p. 104, color illus. p. 105; Chetham,
1969, p. 774.

NOTE
This is one of many studies for the woman in the right
foreground of *Un Dimanche à la Grande Jatte*, 1884-
86, in the collection of The Art Institute of Chicago.
The Smith College Museum of Art owns two other
studies for *La Grande Jatte*, *Three Women* and *Head
of a Woman Sewing*, both conte crayon drawings.

Charles Sheeler
American, 1883-1965

54. Rolling Power
1939
Oil on canvas, 15 x 30 inches
Signed and dated l.r.: *Sheeler 1939*
Purchased 1940:18

PROVENANCE
The Downtown Gallery, New York, to scma.

EXHIBITIONS
New York, The Downtown Gallery, 1940, *Charles
Sheeler: Power*, no. 4; Art Institute of Chicago, 1941-
42, *52nd Annual Exhibition of American Painting
and Sculpture*, no. 183; Deerfield [Massachusetts]
Academy, 1946; Andover, Massachusetts, Addison
Gallery of American Art, 1946, *Charles Sheeler:
Paintings, Drawings and Photographs*; Dayton [Ohio]
Art Institute, 1949, *The Railroad in Painting*, no. 66,
illus.; Dartmouth, 1950; Houston, Contemporary
Arts Association, 1951, *Sheeler, Dove: Exhibition*;
Wesleyan, 1951, no. 17; The Brooklyn Museum,
1952, *Revolution and Tradition*, no. 121; Minneapolis,
Walker Art Center, 1952, *Charles Sheeler*; Los An-
geles, University of California Art Galleries, 1954-55,
Charles Sheeler: A Retrospective Exhibition, no. 22,
[also shown: San Francisco, M.H. De Young Memo-
rial Museum, Fort Worth Art Center, Utica, Munson-
Williams-Proctor Institute of Art, Philadelphia,
Pennsylvania Academy of Fine Arts, and San Diego

Fine Arts Gallery]; Fort Worth Art Center, 1958, *The Iron Horse in Art*, no. 97, illus. fig. 36; Wesleyan, 1958; Minneapolis, Walker Art Center, 1960-61, *The Precisionist View in American Art*, p. 58, illus. p. 39, [also shown: New York, Whitney Museum of American Art, Detroit Institute of Arts, Los Angeles County Museum, and San Francisco Museum of Art]; Middletown, Connecticut, Wesleyan University, Davison Art Center, 1961, *The City and the Land*, no. [23]; Allentown [Pennsylvania] Art Museum, 1961, *Charles Sheeler: Retrospective Exhibition*, no. 25; Iowa City, State University of Iowa, Department of Art, 1963, *The Quest of Charles Sheeler: 83 Works Honoring His 80th Year*, no. 45, p. 22, illus. fig. 12; Minneapolis, 1963-64, illus.; SCMA, *American Painting*, 1964, no. 19, illus.; Albuquerque, University of New Mexico Art Gallery, 1964-65, *The Painter and the Photograph*, no. 42a, pp. 32-33, illus. p. 32 [also shown: Waltham, Massachusetts, Brandeis University, Rose Art Museum, Bloomington, Indiana University, Museum of Art, Iowa City, State University of Iowa Art Gallery, New Orleans, Isaac Delgado Museum of Art, and Santa Barbara (California) Museum of Art]; Bridgeport, Connecticut, Museum of Art, Science and Industry, 1965, *The Machine in Art*, no. 20; Cedar Rapids [Iowa] Art Center, 1967, *Charles Sheeler: A Retrospective Exhibition*, no. 15; Washington, D.C., National Collection of Fine Arts, Philadelphia Museum of Art, and New York, Whitney Museum of American Art, 1968-69, *Charles Sheeler*, no. 90, illus. p. 52; Colby-Currier, 1969, no. 30, illus.

REFERENCES
"Sheeler Paints Power," *Art Digest*, vol. XV, no. 5, December 1, 1940, p. 8; "Power: A Portfolio by Charles Sheeler," *Fortune*, vol. XXII, no. 6, December 1940, pp. 78-79, color illus.; Jere Abbott, "Burchfield and Sheeler for the U.S. Collection at Smith College," *Art News*, vol. XXXIX, no. 11, December 14, 1940, p. 12f, illus. p. 6; "Smith College Museum of Art," *Parnassus*, vol. XIII, no. 1, January 1941, p. 35, illus.; "Sheeler and Power," *Parnassus*, vol. XIII, no. 1, January 1941, p. 46; Richard Boyd Ballou, "The Liberal Arts College and Education," *Smith Alumnae Quarterly*, vol. XXXII, no. 2, February 1941, p. 83; J[ere] A[bbott], "Rolling Power," SCMA *Bulletin*, 1941, pp. 3-4, illus. p. 2; SCMA *Catalogue Supplement*, 1941, p. 6, illus. p. 21; Samuel M. Kootz, *New Frontiers in American Painting*, New York, 1943, illus. no. 77; P.L., "Dayton Presents the Railroad in Paint," *Art Digest*, vol. 23, no. 15, May 1, 1949, p. 16, illus.; *The Brooklyn Museum Bulletin*, vol. XIII, no. 1, Fall 1951, cover illus.; [Sheeler], *Time*, vol. LXV, no. 1, January 3, 1955, p. 64, illus.; George M. Craven, "Sheeler at Seventy-five," *College Art Journal*, vol. XVIII, no. 2, Winter 1959, p. 138, illus. fig. 3, p. 139; Hilton Kramer, "The American Precisionists," *Arts*, vol. 35, no. 6, March 1961, pp. 32-37, illus. p. 37; John I.H. Baur, "Beauty or the Beast? The Machine and American Art," *Art in America*, vol. 48, no. 1, 1960, pp. 82-87, illus. pp. 82-83; Novak, 1969, p. 274, illus.

NOTE
Rolling Power is one of six paintings by Sheeler which were commissioned for reproduction in the December 1940 issue of *Fortune* magazine. Others in the series entitled "Power," were, *Steam Turbine*, *The Yankee Clipper*, *Primitive Power*, *Suspended Power*, and *Conversation—Sky and Earth*. All were exhibited for the first time at The Downtown Gallery, New York in December 1940.

Yves Tanguy
French, 1900-1955

55. *Les Mouvements et les actes*
1937
Oil on canvas, 25½ x 20¾ inches
Signed and dated l.r.: *YVES TANGUY 37*
Given by the estate of Kay Sage Tanguy 1964:45

EXHIBITIONS
New York, Museum of Modern Art, 1955, *Yves Tanguy*, p. 18, illus. p. 38; Amherst, 1968; Colby-Currier, 1969, no. 55, illus.

REFERENCES
Pierre Matisse, *Yves Tanguy*, New York, 1963, no. 199, p. 103, illus.

Dwight W. Tryon
American, 1849-1925

56. *November Evening*
1924
Oil on panel, 20 x 30 inches
Signed and dated, l.l.: *1924 TRYON*,
l.r.: *D W TRYON*
Tryon Bequest 1926:12

EXHIBITIONS
Easthampton, Massachusetts, Williston Academy, 1945.

REFERENCES
Henry C. White, *Life and Art of Dwight William Tryon*, Boston, 1930, illus. pl. [63].

NOTE
This is the last work of the artist.

Edouard Vuillard
French, 1868-1940

57. *Intérieur à l'Etang-la-Ville*
1893
Oil on millboard panel, 12½ x 14⁵⁄₁₆ inches
Signed and dated l.r.: *V 93*
Purchased 1938:15

PROVENANCE
Josse Bernheim; Jacques Seligmann & Co., New York, to SCMA.

EXHIBITIONS
Chicago, AIC, 1938-39, no. 26, illus.; Washington, D.C., Phillips Memorial Gallery, 1939, *Vuillard*, no. 4; New York, Museum of Modern Art, 1944, *Art in Progress*, illus. p. 34; Andover, 1945, no. 27, illus.; Providence, Museum of Art of the Rhode Island School of Design, 1949, *Isms in Art Since 1800*, p. 34, illus. p. 25; Paris, Musée d'Art Moderne, 1952, *L'Oeuvre du XXe siècle*, no. 111; London, Tate Gallery, 1952, *XXth Century Masterpieces*, no. 94; Knoedler, 1953, no. 31; Boston, ICA, 1954, no. [28]; Cleveland Museum of Art and New York, Museum of Modern Art, 1954, *Edouard Vuillard*, p. 16, illus. p. 48; Pittsburgh, Carnegie Institute, 1954, *Pictures of Everyday Life: Genre Painting in Europe 1500-1900*, no. 85, illus.; Chicago, Arts Club, 1961, no. 25, illus.; Minneapolis Institute of Arts, 1962, *The Nabis and Their Circle*, p. 149 [Minneapolis Institute of Arts *Bulletin*, vol. LI, no. 4, December 1962]; Trenton, 1967, no. 109, color illus.; Munich, Haus der Kunst, and Paris, Orangerie des Tuileries, 1968, *Edouard Vuillard—Xavier Roussel*, no. 20, illus. p. 121 and on catalogue cover in color [illus. on poster in color]; Minneapolis Institute of Arts, *The Past Rediscovered: French Painting 1800-1900*, no. 86, illus.; Colby-Currier, 1969, p. vii, no. 26, illus.

REFERENCES
Adolphe Basler and Charles Kunstler, *The Post-Impressionists from Monet to Bonnard*, New York, 1931, illus. pl. 58; Claude Roger-Marx, "A Portrait of Vuillard," *Formes*, no. 23, March 1932, pp. 240-241, illus. following p. 240; Abbott, 1939, p. 7; Jere Abbott, "Intérieur à l'Etang-la-Ville by Vuillard," SCMA *Bulletin*, 1939, pp. 23-24, illus. p. 23; *Smith Alumnae Quarterly*, vol. XXXI, no. 1, November 1939, illus. p. 27; Cheney, 1941, illus. p. 351; SCMA *Catalogue Supplement*, 1941, p. 7, illus. p. 26; Claude Roger-Marx, *Vuillard et son temps*, Paris, 1945, p. 52, illus. p. 33; SCMA *Bulletin*, 1947, p. 1; Claude Roger-

Marx, *Vuillard,* Paris, 1948, illus. p. 31; SCMA, *Forty French Pictures,* 1953, no. 33, pp. iv, vii, xxiv-xxv, illus.; *Art Digest,* vol. 27, no. 13, April 1, 1953, illus. p. 14; Robert Goldwater, "Vuillard's Intimate Art," *Art Digest,* vol. 28, no. 9, February 1954, pp. 6-8, illus. fig. 2; Jacques Salomon, *Vuillard admiré,* Paris, 1961, illus. p. 40; Chetham, 1969, p. 774, illus. p. 772; *Encyclopaedia Britannica,* Chicago, 1970, vol. 15, illus. p. 630B.

NOTE
In a letter to the Museum dated 22 November 1967, Antoine Salomon, Vuillard's grand-nephew, identifies the figures in the painting as his grandfather, K.X. Roussel, and Marie Vuillard, the artist's sister, a short time before their marriage in 1893.

James Abbott McNeill Whistler
American, 1834-1903

58. *Portrait of Mrs. Lewis Jarvis* (Ada M. Jarvis)
1878-1879
Oil on canvas, 25 x 16 inches
Purchased 1908:2

PROVENANCE
Mr. and Mrs. Lewis Jarvis, Blenham, Bedfordshire (with Mrs. Jarvis until after 1905); M. Knoedler & Co., New York, to SCMA.

EXHIBITIONS
London, New Gallery, Regent Street (International Society of Painters, Sculptors, and Gravers), 1905, *Memorial Exhibition of the Works of the Late James McNeill Whistler,* no. 65; University of Rochester, Memorial Art Gallery, 1913, *Inaugural Exhibition,* no. 134; Boston, Museum of Fine Arts, 1934, *Exhibition of Oils, Water-Colors, Drawings, and Prints by James McNeill Whistler,* no. 13; Pittsfield, Massachusetts, The Berkshire Museum, 1934, [Single picture loan]; New London, Connecticut, Lyman Allyn

Museum, 1949, *James McNeill Whistler,* no. 1; Columbus [Ohio] Gallery of Fine Arts, 1950, *Masterpieces of Painting,* no. 39 [catalogue published in: The Columbus Gallery of Fine Arts *Bulletin,* vol. XXI, no. 1]; Williams, 1950; The Brooklyn Museum, 1957-58, *Face of America,* no. 59; SCMA, *Portraits,* 1962, no. 17; Chicago, NDC, 1964, no. 33; Art Institute of Chicago and Utica, Munson-Williams-Proctor Institute, 1968, *James McNeill Whistler,* no. 29, illus.; Colby-Currier, 1969, no. 7, illus.

REFERENCES
T.R. Way and G.R. Dennis, *The Art of James McNeill Whistler,* London, 1903, p. 50; E.L. Cary, *The Works of James McNeill Whistler: A Study with a Tentative List of the Artist's Works,* New York, 1907, p. 218; Bernard Sickert, *Whistler,* London, New York, 1908, no. 170; T.R. Way, *Memories of James McNeill Whistler the Artist,* London, 1912, p. 115; Churchill, 1916, p. 16; N.J. Pousette-Dart, *James McN. Whistler,* New York, 1924, n.p., illus.; SCMA *Handbook,* 1925, p. 33, illus., frontispiece; SCMA *Catalogue,* 1937, p. 12, illus. p. 67; James W. Lane, *Whistler,* New York, 1942, p. 95, illus.; SCMA *Bulletin,* 1951, p. 31.

NOTE
Bankrupt, Whistler left London for Venice in September, 1879, soon after his libel suit against Ruskin, on commission from the Fine Arts Society for a series of etchings. Thomas Way (*loc. cit.*) says Mrs. Jarvis' portrait was painted "just before he went to Venice," and an unpublished letter from the painter to Mrs. Jarvis dated September 6, 1879 which was acquired with the picture confirms this date. He speaks of the portrait as follows: "The little head ought to have been more charming—but I did my best at the time which I am afraid was very poor." He also speaks of having a frame made (it is still with the picture) and having the portrait sent to Mr. & Mrs. Jarvis in Bedfordshire.

Illustrations

1. ANONYMOUS French, 19th Century, *Portrait of a Youth*, c. 1815

2. ALBERT BIERSTADT American, 1830-1902, *A Wilderness Lake*, 1861

3. RALPH ALBERT BLAKELOCK American, 1847-1919, *Outlet of a Mountain Lake*, c. 1887

4. Attributed to RICHARD PARKES BONINGTON English, 1801–1828, *View of a Norman Town*, c. 1827–28

5. PIERRE BONNARD French, 1867-1947, *Les Toits*, c. 1897

6. PIERRE BONNARD French, 1867-1947, *Paysage du Midi*, 1931

7. EUGENE BOUDIN French, 1824-1898, *Still Life with Fish and Oysters*, c. 1854-1858

8. PAUL CEZANNE French, 1839-1906, *La Route tournante à La Roche-Guyon*, c. 1885

9. JAMES WELLS CHAMPNEY American, 1843-1903, *Boon Companions*, 1879

10. WILLIAM MERRITT CHASE American, 1849-1916, *Woman in Black*, c. 1881

11. JEAN-BAPTISTE CAMILLE COROT French, 1796-1875, *Jumièges*, c. 1830

12. JEAN-BAPTISTE CAMILLE COROT French, 1796-1875, *La Blonde Gasconne*, c. 1850

13. JEAN-BAPTISTE CAMILLE COROT French, 1796-1875, *Dubuisson's Grove at Brunoy*, 1868

14. GUSTAVE COURBET French, 1819-1877, *La Toilette de la mariée*, c. 1858

15. GUSTAVE COURBET French, 1819-1877, *Portrait of M. Nodler, the Elder, at Trouville, 1865*

16. EDGAR HILAIRE GERMAIN DEGAS French, 1834-1917, *Portrait of René de Gas*, c. 1855

17. EDGAR HILAIRE GERMAIN DEGAS French, 1834-1917, *Dancer on the Stage*, c. 1877-1880

18. NARCISSE VIRGILE DIAZ DE LA PENA French, 1808-1876, *Forest Pool, Barbizon*, 1862

19. THOMAS EAKINS American, 1844-1916, *In Grandmother's Time*, 1876

20. THOMAS EAKINS American, 1844-1916, *Portrait of Mrs. Edith Mahon*, 1904

21. EDWIN ROMANZO ELMER American, 1850-1923, *Mourning Picture*, c. 1889

22. HENRI FANTIN-LATOUR French, 1836-1904, *Portrait of Mr. Becker*, 1886

23. PAUL GAUGUIN French, 1848-1903, *Banlieue Parisienne*, 1879

24. ANNE-LOUIS GIRODET DE ROUCY-TRIOSON French, 1767–1824
Portrait of Madame Benoit-François Trioson(?), 1804

25. JUAN GRIS Spanish, 1887-1927, *Still Life: The Bottle of Rum*, c. 1914

26. JUAN GRIS Spanish, 1887-1927, *Fruit Dish and Bottle*, 1916

27. CHILDE HASSAM American, 1859-1935, *Union Square in Spring*, 1896

28. WINSLOW HOMER American, 1836-1910, *Shipbuilding at Gloucester*, 1871

29. WILLIAM MORRIS HUNT American, 1824-1879, *Portrait of William Sidney Thayer*, c. 1860

30. JEAN AUGUSTE DOMINIQUE INGRES French, 1780-1867, *The Death of Leonardo da Vinci* c. 1818

31. ERNST LUDWIG KIRCHNER German, 1880–1938,
    Dodo and Her Brother, c. 1908

32. FRANZ KLINE American, 1910-1962, *Rose, Purple and Black*, 1958

33. FERNAND LEGER French, 1881-1955, *Elément mécanique I*, 1924

34. EDOUARD MANET French, 1832-1883, *Portrait of Marguérite de Conflans*, 1873

35. ALFRED HENRY MAURER American, 1868-1932, *Le Bal Bullier*, c. 1904

36. GEORGES MICHEL French, 1763-1843, *Landscape*

37. JEAN-FRANCOIS MILLET French, 1814-1875, *Portrait of William Morris Hunt*, c. 1853-55

38. JEAN-FRANCOIS MILLET French, 1814-1875, *Farm at Gréville*, c. 1871

39. CLAUDE MONET French, 1840-1926, *The Seine at Bougival*, 1869

40. CLAUDE MONET French, 1840-1926, *Field of Poppies*, 1890

41. CLAUDE MONET French, 1840-1926, *Cathedral at Rouen*, 1894

42. GIORGIO MORANDI Italian, 1890-1964, *Still Life*, 1954

43. JOHN FREDERICK PETO American, 1854-1907, *Discarded Treasures*, c. 1904

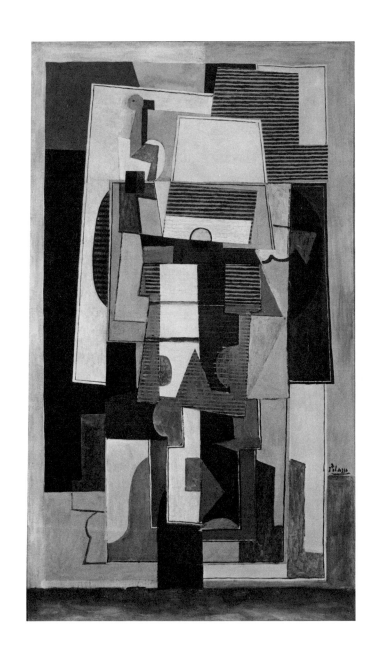

44. PABLO PICASSO Spanish, 1881-   , *La Table*, 1919-1920

45. PABLO PICASSO Spanish, 1881-   , *Les Misérables (Les Pauvres au bord de la mer)* 1903

46. WILLIAM MATTHEW PRIOR American, 1806-1873, *Mount Vernon and the Tomb of Washington*, c. 1855

47. PIERRE AUGUSTE RENOIR French, 1841-1919, *Portrait of Mme. Edouard Maître*, c. 1871

48. ANTON ROMAKO Austrian, 1832-1889, *Girl on a Swing*, c. 1882

49. HENRI ROUSSEAU French, 1844-1910, *Banks of the Oise*, 1905

50. **PIERRE ETIENNE THEODORE ROUSSEAU** French, 1812-1867, *The Bridge at Moret*, c. 1828-1829

51. ALBERT PINKHAM RYDER American, 1847-1917, *Perrette*, c. 1890

52. JOHN SINGER SARGENT American, 1856-1925, *My Dining Room*, c. 1889

53. GEORGES SEURAT French, 1859-1891, *Woman with a Monkey*, 1884

54. CHARLES SHEELER American, 1883-1965, *Rolling Power*, 1939

55. YVES TANGUY French, 1900-1955, *Les Mouvements et les actes*, 1937

56. DWIGHT W. TRYON American, 1849-1925, *November Evening*, 1924

57. EDOUARD VUILLARD French, 1868-1940, *Intérieur à l'Etang-la-Ville*, 1893

58. JAMES ABBOTT MC NEILL WHISTLER American, 1834-1903,
Portrait of Mrs. Lewis Jarvis, 1878-1879

Museum Visiting Committee

In 1951, following a suggestion from the College's Board of Counsellors, a Visiting Committee to the Museum was formed by Mrs. John Wintersteen (Bernice McIlhenny '25) and the director of the Museum, Mr. Hitchcock. The members were chosen for their eminence as museum professionals or as collectors. Since that date the Museum's policies have been guided by this body. To them is due considerable credit for the enlargement of interest in the collection and for the many important gifts which have come to it.

Former Members

W.G. Russell Allen: 1951-1955
Mrs. John Cowles (Elizabeth M. Bates '22): 1951-1954
Mrs. Charles C. Cunningham (Eleanor A. Lamont '32): 1951-1960
Mrs. Henry T. Curtiss (Mina Kirstein '18): 1963-1969
Ernest Gottlieb: 1956-1969
Philip Hofer: 1951-1968
Mrs. Maurice Lazarus (Nancy Stix '42): 1951-1969
Stanley Marcus: 1955-1962

Current Members

Jere Abbott, *Chairman*
Mrs. Roger Williams Bennett (Margaret Goldthwait '21)
David S. Brooke
Mrs. Holger Cahill (Dorothy Miller '25 Hon. L.H.D. '59)
Mrs. Malcolm G. Chace, Jr. (Beatrice Oenslager '28)
Mrs. Ralph F. Colin (Georgia Talmey '28)
Charles C. Cunningham
Mrs. Priscilla Cunningham (Priscilla Cunningham '58)

Dorothy Dudley
Selma Erving '27
Mrs. John Jakobson (Barbara Petschesky '54)
Mrs. Sigmund Kunstadter (Maxine Weil '24)
A. Hyatt Mayor
Agnes Mongan (A.M. '29, Hon. L.H.D. '41)
Mrs. James E. Pollak (Mabel S. Brown '27)
James Thrall Soby
Mrs. John Wintersteen (Bernice McIlhenny '25)

Former Directors of the Museum

Alfred Vance Churchill	1920-1932
Jere Abbott	1932-1946
Frederick Hartt (Acting Director)	1946-1947
Edgar Schenck	1947-1949
Henry-Russell Hitchcock	1949-1955
Robert O. Parks	1955-1961
Patricia Milne-Henderson (Acting Assistant Director)	1961-1962

Staff of the Museum

Charles Chetham, *Director*
Michael J. Wentworth, *Assistant Director, Curator of Prints, Acting Director (1969-70)*
Mira M. Fabian, *Assistant Curator*
Anna H. Kennick, *Registrar*
Jane M. Watts, *Acting Registrar (1969-70)*
Ernestine J. Stieber, *Administrative Assistant*
Wilda M. Craig, *Museum Members Secretary*
Helen M. Sullivan, *Receptionist*
Doris H. La Riviere, *Receptionist*
Edward D. Russell, *Technician*

Photographic Credits

All photographs by Hyman Edelstein, Northampton
    except the following:
Marjorie de Wolf Laurent, Northampton: nos. 4, 57.
Wendell Ray, Waterville, Maine: nos. 17, 36.
Smith College Archives: figs. 1, 3, 5, 9, 10.
Allison Spence, Northampton: no. 6 and figs.
    2, 4, 7, 12.
Alan Spencer, New York: nos. 5, 16, 35, 38, 42, 47.
    59, 50, 51, 53, 54.
Herbert P. Vose, Wellesley Hills, Mass.: nos. 3, 11,
    and figs. 13, 17, 22, 23, 24.

*6,500 copies of this catalogue, designed by Richard
Hendel, have been printed by The Meriden Gravure
Company in April 1970 for the Smith College Museum of Art on the occasion of the American Federation of Arts' circulating exhibition "Masterpieces
from the Collection of the Smith College Museum
of Art"*